best-loved extra easy recipes

a collection of *perfection*

What's your favourite Slimming World recipe? Maybe it's fish and chips, pizza-topped chicken, swede-topped cottage pie or a sweet sensation like Mississippi mud pie… or perhaps you love too many of them to choose! Well, this amazing new cookbook will give you more choice than ever before, as it brings together all of our most popular dishes – it's your very own Slimming World kitchen bible!

Choosing the 80 timelessly tasty classics for this book wasn't easy. We combed through your letters, emails, website comments and Facebook messages, and we looked at the online recipes you use most (last year our brilliant beef lasagne was number one – see p48). Then we garnished the list with a sprinkling of delights that just had to be included, like aromatic duck wraps and Slimming World sausage Scotch eggs!

As well as chapters on meat, poultry and fish that are full of Food Optimising favourites, you'll find starters and light bites, veggie main courses, pasta sauces and sensational sides… not forgetting those luscious low-Syn puddings that make a meal unforgettable.

So a warm welcome to *Best-loved Extra Easy Recipes* – we guarantee it will be the first book off the shelf next time your stomach starts to rumble!

contents

starters / orders

Whether you want stunning starters, satisfying snacks or brilliant breakfasts, you'll find loads of Syn-free and low-Syn inspiration here.

overnight oats

serves 1

6 Syns per serving

ready in 5 minutes,
plus overnight soaking

35g plain porridge oats

200g fat free natural yogurt

mixed berries, such as
strawberries, raspberries,
blueberries or blackberries

cinnamon, to dust (optional)

This classic Slimming World breakfast is an unbeatable way to start your day! Swap the berries for your favourite fruits or change the yogurt for your favourite Free variety.

Spoon layers of porridge oats, yogurt and most of the fruit into a bowl. Cover and chill overnight so that the porridge absorbs the yogurt.

In the morning, stir to mix all the layers together, top with the remaining fruit and dust with cinnamon, if using, to serve.

Have the oats as a Healthy Extra b choice to make this breakfast Free!

ham and egg muffins

makes 8

Free

ready in 40 minutes,
plus cooling

___

low calorie cooking spray

250g chestnut mushrooms,
sliced

120g lean ham, visible fat
removed, roughly chopped

half a bunch of spring onions,
finely chopped

8 eggs

50ml skimmed milk

salt and freshly ground
black pepper

Try these simple and delicious Free 'muffins' for breakfast, as an anytime snack or as a meal with baked beans and grilled tomatoes.

Preheat your oven to 200°C/Fan 180°C/Gas 6.

Spray a non-stick frying pan with low calorie cooking spray and cook the mushrooms for 10 minutes or until golden. Stir in the ham and spring onions.

Whisk the eggs and milk in a bowl and season to taste.

Line eight holes of a muffin tin with paper cases. Spoon the mushroom mixture into the cases and pour in the egg. Bake for 20-25 minutes or until slightly risen and golden.

Leave to cool slightly before removing the muffins from the cases.

If you have a good non-stick muffin tin, you won't need to use paper cases. Just spray the holes with low calorie cooking spray before spooning in the mushroom mixture.

prawn cocktail

serves 4

1 Syn per serving

ready in 10 minutes

Chunky prawns in a punchy sauce make this everyone's favourite retro starter. Turning back the clock has never been so tasty!

juice of 1 lemon, plus wedges to serve

4 level tbsp extra-light mayonnaise

125g fat free natural fromage frais

2 tbsp passata

a few drops of Tabasco

salt and freshly ground black pepper

450g cooked and peeled king or tiger prawns, with or without tails

2 Little Gem lettuces, leaves separated and roughly torn

smoked paprika, to dust

small handful of finely chopped fresh chives and dill plus a few chives, to garnish

Mix the lemon juice, mayonnaise, fromage frais, passata and Tabasco in a bowl. Season to taste, add the prawns and stir well.

Divide the lettuce leaves between cocktail glasses and spoon in the prawn mixture. Dust with paprika, scatter over the herbs and serve with lemon wedges to squeeze over.

chicken soup

Some people claim that this timeless broth is a cure for the common cold and whether that's true or not, it certainly tastes sensational!

Put the chicken in a large pan and just cover with cold water. Bring to the boil over a high heat and skim off any scum from the top.

Add the celery, onions, roughly chopped carrots and leeks, parsley stalks and stock. Season with pepper, turn the heat to low and simmer gently for 1 hour.

Meanwhile, cook the pearl barley according to the packet instructions.

Pick the meat off the chicken bones, roughly shred and keep warm.

Strain the soup through a fine sieve, discarding anything left in the sieve. Return the soup to the pan, add the finely chopped carrot and sliced leek and cook for 10 minutes or until the vegetables are soft.

Stir the shredded chicken and pearl barley into the soup, heat through and season to taste. Finely chop the parsley leaves and scatter over the soup to serve.

To skin a chicken drumstick, peel away a little skin from the thick end and pull it off over the bony end (use kitchen paper to help you get a good grip).

serves 4

Free

ready in 1 hour 20 minutes

800g chicken thighs and drumsticks, skinned (see tip)

2 celery sticks, roughly chopped

2 onions, roughly chopped

3 carrots – 2 roughly chopped and 1 peeled and finely chopped

3 leeks – 2 roughly chopped and 1 finely sliced

small bunch of fresh parsley, stalks and leaves separated

1.2 litres boiling chicken stock

salt and freshly ground black pepper

75g dried pearl barley

thai fish cakes
with coriander sauce

serves 4

1½ Syns per serving

❄ (uncooked fish cakes only)

ready in 45 minutes,
plus chilling

400g floury potatoes, such as
Maris Piper, peeled and
roughly chopped

350g skinless and boneless
white fish fillets

2 garlic cloves, crushed

bunch of spring onions,
finely sliced

small handful of finely
chopped fresh coriander

small handful of finely
chopped fresh mint

1 lemongrass stick, outer leaves
removed, finely chopped

1 red chilli, deseeded and
finely chopped

2cm piece of root ginger,
peeled and grated

4 level tbsp extra-light
mayonnaise

low calorie cooking spray

for the coriander sauce

1 red chilli, deseeded

half a bunch of spring onions

large handful of fresh coriander

grated zest and juice of
1 lime, plus wedges to serve

juice of 1 orange

The fresh flavours of lime, ginger and lemongrass
are at the heart of Thai food and our zesty sauce is
the perfect accompaniment for these tasty cakes.

Boil the potatoes in a pan of lightly salted water for 15 minutes or
until tender.

Meanwhile, put the fish, garlic, spring onions, coriander, mint, lemongrass,
chilli and ginger into a food processor and blitz briefly to mix together.
Add the mayonnaise and mix again. Tip the mixture into a large bowl.

Drain the potatoes and return to the pan. Mash until fairly smooth then
tip into the bowl with the fish and mix well.

Divide the mixture into 12 equal portions and form each one into a flat
cake. Arrange the cakes in a roasting tin lined with non-stick baking
parchment, cover and chill for 4 hours or overnight if possible.

Preheat the oven to 190°C/Fan 170°C/Gas 5.

Spray the fish cakes with low calorie cooking spray and roast for
15-20 minutes or until lightly browned and cooked through.

While the fish cakes are in the oven, put all the sauce ingredients in a
food processor and blitz well. Add enough water to get the consistency
you want and blitz again.

Serve the fish cakes hot with the sauce and lime wedges to squeeze over.

aromatic duck wraps

Shredded duck wrapped in pancakes is one of the highlights of a Chinese takeaway. Now you can make them at home with the Syns shredded as well as the duck!

Pull the skin off the duck legs using kitchen paper to help you get a good grip, trimming off any remaining skin and fat with kitchen scissors.

Put the duck legs, ginger, star anise and all but 1 tablespoon of the soy sauce in a deep non-stick frying pan. Add enough cold water to almost cover the duck. Bring to the boil over a high heat, then reduce the heat to low and cook for 1 hour or until the duck is very tender.

Preheat the oven to 200°C/Fan 180°C/Gas 6.

Drain the duck legs thoroughly, put them on a baking tray and brush with 1 level tablespoon of the hoisin sauce. Roast for 15 minutes or until browned and sticky. Set aside to cool.

Meanwhile, make the sauce. Mix the remaining hoisin sauce and soy sauce with 2 tablespoons of water in a small bowl.

When the duck is cool enough to handle, take the flesh off the bone and shred it with two forks.

Lay everything out on a table and invite everyone to help themselves. To assemble a wrap, put some cucumber, spring onion and duck into a lettuce leaf and spoon in a little sauce.

serves 4
(makes about 20 wraps)

1 Syn per serving

ready in 1 hour 30 minutes, plus cooling

---

4 duck legs

2.5cm piece of root ginger, peeled and sliced

2 star anise

150ml soy sauce

3 level tbsp hoisin sauce

1 cucumber, deseeded and cut into matchsticks, to serve

bunch of spring onions, thinly shredded, to serve

4 Little Gem lettuces, leaves separated, to serve

sweetcorn
and chive fritters

serves 4 (makes 20)

Free

ready in 20 minutes

---

3 eggs, lightly beaten

6 spring onions – 3 roughly chopped and 3 finely sliced

340g can sweetcorn, drained

salt and freshly ground black pepper

small handful of finely chopped fresh chives

low calorie cooking spray

½ red chilli, deseeded and finely chopped, to garnish

lime wedges, to serve

These nourishing nibbles are a joy to eat and so simple to make – you'll want to enjoy them again and again.

Put the eggs, the roughly chopped spring onions and three-quarters of the sweetcorn in a food processor. Season to taste, blitz to combine and transfer to a large bowl. Stir in most of the chives, the finely sliced spring onions and the remaining sweetcorn.

Spray a large non-stick frying pan with low calorie cooking spray and place over a medium-high heat. When the pan is hot, drop in heaped tablespoons of the mixture and cook for 1-2 minutes on each side or until lightly golden and cooked through (you might need to do this in batches). Drain on kitchen paper and repeat until you have used up all of the mixture.

Scatter over the chilli and remaining chives and serve with lime wedges to squeeze over.

peppered feta and melon salad

You might not have thought of putting them together but creamy, salty feta cheese goes brilliantly with refreshing melon and watermelon in this simple starter.

Thickly slice the watermelon and melon, then cut off the skin and remove the seeds. Cut the flesh into cubes and divide between plates.

Scatter the feta on top, grind over plenty of black pepper and scatter with mint to serve.

serves 4

3 Syns per serving

ready in 15 minutes

½ small watermelon, chilled

1 small honeydew melon, chilled

130g reduced fat feta cheese, cubed

freshly ground black pepper

small handful of roughly chopped fresh mint, to garnish

tomato soup

serves 4

Free

ready in 30 minutes

---

1 red onion, chopped

1 carrot, peeled and chopped

1 celery stick, chopped

3 x 400g cans plum tomatoes

2 tbsp tomato purée

1 tbsp sweetener

600ml boiling vegetable stock

salt and freshly ground
black pepper

handful of finely chopped
fresh basil, plus a few leaves
to garnish

4 tbsp quark, to serve

Tomato soup is so soothing and satisfying – and it's even more delicious when you make it yourself.

Put the onion, carrot, celery, tomatoes, tomato purée, sweetener and stock in a saucepan. Bring to the boil over a high heat then cover, turn the heat to low and simmer for 20 minutes.

Take off the heat and leave to cool slightly. Blend until smooth using a food processor or stick blender, season to taste and stir in the basil. Ladle the soup into bowls.

Thin down the quark with a little water and add a swirl to each bowl, grind over a little black pepper and garnish with basil leaves to serve.

meat masterclass

Magnificent meat is delicious and satisfying, and it takes a starring role in so many of our favourite meals – from juicy burgers and filling lasagne to Lancashire hotpot and the Sunday roast.

swede-topped cottage pie

serves 4

Free

ready in 1 hour

Cottage pie is as comforting as it gets and it's so easy to make. Our seriously tasty version has a mashed swede topping so it's perfect for Extra Easy *SP* too!

1kg swede, peeled and roughly chopped

salt and freshly ground black pepper

low calorie cooking spray

1 red onion, finely chopped

2 garlic cloves, crushed

2 celery sticks, finely chopped

2 carrots, peeled and finely chopped

500g lean beef mince (5% fat or less)

400g can chopped tomatoes

1 tbsp vegetable stock

1 tsp sweetener

2 tsp dried oregano

1 egg, lightly beaten

Cook the swede in a saucepan of lightly salted boiling water for 15 minutes or until tender. Drain, return to the pan and mash until smooth. Season to taste and set aside.

Meanwhile, spray a large non-stick frying pan with low calorie cooking spray and place over a high heat. Add the onion, garlic, celery and carrots and stir-fry for 5 minutes. Add the mince and stir-fry for 5 minutes, then add the tomatoes, stock, sweetener and oregano and stir well. Bring to the boil and remove from the heat.

Preheat the oven to 200°C/Fan 180°C/Gas 6.

Transfer the beef mixture to a casserole dish and spread the mashed swede over the top, smoothing the surface with a fork (add a pattern if you like!). Brush with the beaten egg and bake for 25-30 minutes or until lightly golden and bubbling.

Serve hot with your favourite vegetables.

cheese and bacon burgers

serves 4

7½ Syns per serving

❋ (uncooked burgers only)

ready in 30 minutes

---

1 onion, finely chopped

2 garlic cloves, crushed

500g lean beef mince (5% fat or less)

1 tbsp Worcestershire sauce

salt and freshly ground black pepper

low calorie cooking spray

8 back bacon rashers, visible fat removed

40g reduced fat Cheddar-style cheese, thinly sliced

4 x 60g wholemeal rolls, split and toasted

2 tomatoes, sliced

lettuce leaves

cucumber, sliced

4 tbsp passata

With crispy bacon, melting cheese, fresh salad and a prime patty of lean, juicy beef, our indulgent cheeseburger has got the lot.

Preheat the grill to high.

Put the onion, garlic, beef and Worcestershire sauce in a bowl, season to taste and combine using your fingers. Divide the mixture into four portions and shape each one into a burger.

Put the burgers on the grill pan, spray with low calorie cooking spray and grill for 10-12 minutes or until cooked through, turning once. Grill the bacon alongside the burgers until done to your liking, and top the burgers with the cheese for the last 2 minutes of the cooking time to melt.

Fill each roll with tomato, lettuce, cucumber, two bacon rashers, a burger and the passata. Grind over a little black pepper and serve hot with Slimming World chips (see page 140) and salad.

Leave out the roll or have it as a Healthy Extra b choice to save 6 Syns.

beef and pumpkin
stir-fry

serves 4

Free

ready in 40 minutes

---

low calorie cooking spray

2 onions, thickly sliced

½ pumpkin or 1 butternut squash, peeled, deseeded and cubed

600g lean beef steak, visible fat removed

4 tbsp soy sauce

1 tsp sweetener

1 bird's-eye chilli, deseeded and chopped

3cm piece of root ginger, peeled and grated

2 tbsp Thai fish sauce (nam pla)

1 star anise

1 tsp Chinese five-spice powder

1 tbsp oyster sauce

half a bunch of spring onions, shredded, to garnish

small handful of roughly chopped fresh coriander, to garnish

This wonderfully warming stir-fry is packed with all the things that make Asian food so more-ish. Don't worry if you can't get pumpkin – squash is a very satisfying substitute.

Spray a non-stick wok or frying pan with low calorie cooking spray and place over a medium-high heat. Add the onions and pumpkin or squash and stir-fry for 4-5 minutes. Cover and cook gently for 8-10 minutes or until just tender. Transfer to a plate and keep warm.

Meanwhile, put the beef between sheets of cling film and beat with a mallet or heavy pan until thin. Cut into thin strips.

Put the soy sauce, sweetener, chilli, ginger, Thai fish sauce, star anise, five-spice powder and oyster sauce into the wok and cook over a medium heat for 3-4 minutes.

Add the beef to the wok, turn the heat to high and cook for 3-4 minutes or until just cooked through. Stir in the onions and pumpkin or squash and cook for 1 minute. Discard the star anise if you like.

Scatter over the spring onions and coriander and serve hot.

italian meatballs
in tomato sauce

Our mouth-watering meatballs are packed with a beautiful beefiness that the whole family will love.

Preheat the grill to hot.

Put the beef, onion, garlic, oregano, egg, most of the chopped basil and some seasoning in a large bowl and mix well. Divide into 24 equal portions then, using your hands, roll each portion into a ball and spread them out on the grill pan. Grill for 10 minutes or until the meatballs start to brown.

Meanwhile, put all the ingredients for the tomato sauce in a lidded saucepan, season to taste and bring to the boil over a high heat. Reduce the heat to low and simmer gently for 10 minutes.

Add the meatballs to the tomato sauce, cover the saucepan and simmer gently for another 15 minutes or until the meatballs are cooked through.

Scatter the remaining chopped basil and the basil leaves over the meatballs and sauce and serve hot with your favourite vegetables.

serves 4
Free

ready in 45 minutes

750g lean beef mince (5% fat or less)

1 small onion, finely chopped

2 garlic cloves, crushed

1 tsp dried oregano

1 egg, beaten

large handful of chopped fresh basil, plus a few leaves to garnish

salt and freshly ground black pepper

for the tomato sauce

1 onion, finely chopped

2 garlic cloves, crushed

2 x 400g cans chopped tomatoes (or use half canned tomatoes, half passata)

1 tbsp tomato purée

½ tsp sweetener

easy meatloaf
with barbecue sauce

serves 6

1 Syn per serving

ready in 1 hour

500g lean beef mince
(5% fat or less)

500g lean pork mince
(5% fat or less)

2 onions, roughly chopped

1 red pepper, deseeded

1 garlic clove, crushed

1 tbsp passata

salt and freshly ground
black pepper

2 medium slices of bread from
a small 400g wholemeal loaf,
crusts removed

2 tbsp skimmed milk

1 egg

small handful of mixed fresh
herbs, such as parsley and mint

for the barbecue sauce

1 tsp barbecue seasoning

1 level tbsp brown sauce

1 level tbsp tomato ketchup

1 tbsp Worcestershire sauce

200g passata

1 tbsp dark soy sauce

Our meatloaf is a doddle to prepare and it's so handy to have in the fridge! Anything left over makes a fantastic lunchbox filler.

Preheat the oven to 220°C/Fan 200°C/Gas 7.

Put the beef, pork, onions, pepper, garlic and passata in a large food processor, season to taste and blitz to a rough texture.

Soak the bread in the milk, squeeze out any excess liquid and add the bread to the food processor along with the egg and most of the mixed herbs. Blitz again to bind everything together, then press the mixture evenly into a large loaf tin and bake for 35-40 minutes.

Meanwhile, mix all the barbecue sauce ingredients together in a bowl and set aside until needed.

Take the meatloaf out of the oven and leave to stand for a few minutes then turn out on to a chopping board. Finely chop the remaining herbs and scatter them over the meatloaf. Slice thickly and serve hot with the barbecue sauce and salad.

steak frites
with salsa

This French brasserie classic is the perfect way to enjoy a perfect steak and crisp, tasty fries – and our low-Syn version is served with a fresh, zesty salsa and a classic French salad.

Preheat your oven to 200°C/Fan 180°C/Gas 6 and line a baking sheet with baking parchment.

Cook the fries in a pan of lightly salted boiling water for 2 minutes, then drain, return to the pan and shake to rough up the edges a bit. Spread out the fries on the baking sheet, spray with low calorie cooking spray and season with salt. Cook in the oven for 12-15 minutes or until golden.

Meanwhile, mix all the ingredients for the salsa in a bowl and set aside.

Place a non-stick griddle pan over a high heat. Season the steaks on both sides and spray lightly with low calorie cooking spray. When the griddle pan is smoking, fry the steaks to your liking (2 minutes each side for rare, 3 minutes each side for medium and 4 minutes each side for well done).

Leave the steaks to rest on kitchen paper for a few minutes then serve hot with the fries, watercress and salsa.

makes 4
Free
ready in 30 minutes

1kg floury potatoes, such as Maris Piper or King Edward, peeled and cut into fries

low calorie cooking spray

salt and freshly ground black pepper

4 lean beef steaks, visible fat removed

bag of watercress salad, to serve

for the salsa

1 bottled roasted red pepper, drained and finely chopped

2 tomatoes, deseeded and finely chopped

2 gherkins, finely chopped

½ red onion, finely chopped

juice of 2 lemons

1 tbsp finely chopped fresh tarragon

spaghetti bolognese

serves 4

Free

❄ (bolognese sauce only)

ready in 50 minutes

---

low calorie cooking spray

2 back bacon rashers, visible
fat removed, roughly chopped

2 onions, roughly chopped

2 carrots, peeled and diced

2 celery sticks,
roughly chopped

2 garlic cloves, crushed

500g lean beef mince
(5% fat or less)

2 x 400g cans chopped
tomatoes

2 tsp dried oregano

1 beef stock cube

500g dried spaghetti

salt and freshly ground
black pepper

small handful of finely
chopped fresh parsley,
to garnish

Our Food Optimised version of the ever-popular Italian dish is simmered slowly with a little bit of bacon to give a lovely depth of flavour.

Spray a large non-stick frying pan with low calorie cooking spray and place over a medium-high heat. Add the bacon, onions, carrots, celery and garlic and stir-fry for about 7 minutes.

Add the beef, breaking it up with a spoon, and cook for 3 minutes until browned. Drain off any excess fat then add the chopped tomatoes and oregano, crumble in the stock cube and bring to the boil. Cover, reduce the heat to low and simmer for 30 minutes.

Meanwhile, cook the spaghetti according to the packet instructions. Drain and keep warm.

Divide the spaghetti and bolognese between shallow bowls, season to taste and scatter over the parsley. Serve hot with salad.

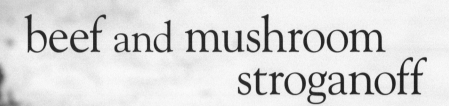

beef and mushroom stroganoff

serves 4

2½ Syns per serving

ready in 30 minutes

---

low calorie cooking spray

1 large red onion, sliced

500g button mushrooms, sliced

2 garlic cloves, crushed

200ml boiling chicken stock

2 tsp green peppercorns in brine, drained

1 tbsp Worcestershire sauce

salt and freshly ground black pepper

400g lean beef steak, visible fat removed, cut into thin strips

120g reduced fat crème fraîche

60g cocktail gherkins or cornichons, drained and chopped

small handful of finely chopped fresh parsley

This traditional dish has been delighting Russians since the 19th century thanks to a creamy sauce bursting with punchy peppercorns and gherkins.

Spray a large lidded non-stick frying pan with low calorie cooking spray and place over a medium heat. Add the onion and mushrooms and stir-fry for 3-4 minutes.

Add the garlic, stock, peppercorns and Worcestershire sauce, cover and simmer for 3-4 minutes. Season the beef strips to taste, stir them in and simmer for 3-4 minutes.

Stir in the crème fraîche and cook gently for 2-3 minutes. Add the cocktail gherkins and most of the parsley and stir well. Check the seasoning, scatter over the remaining parsley and serve hot with tagliatelle pasta or rice plus your favourite vegetables.

beef lasagne

serves 4

1 Syn per serving

ready in 1 hour 15 minutes

500g lean beef mince
(5% fat or less)

1 red pepper, deseeded and
cut into bite-sized chunks

1 courgette, cubed

1 onion, finely chopped

4 garlic cloves, crushed

400g can chopped tomatoes

400g passata

2 tsp dried mixed herbs

salt and freshly ground
black pepper

500g fat free natural yogurt

2 eggs, lightly beaten

a pinch of nutmeg

low calorie cooking spray

12 dried lasagne sheets

4 level tbsp freshly grated
Parmesan cheese

This Italian favourite was the most searched-for recipe on our website last year… and you'll know why after your first mouthful!

Place a large non-stick frying pan over a high heat. Add the beef, cook for a few minutes and drain off any fat in the pan. Add the pepper, courgette, onion and garlic and stir-fry for 6-8 minutes. Add the tomatoes, passata and dried herbs, season to taste and turn the heat to medium. Cook for 12-15 minutes, stirring often.

Meanwhile, mix the yogurt, eggs and nutmeg until smooth. Season to taste and set aside.

Preheat the oven to 200°C/Fan 180°C/Gas 6.

Spray a medium-sized ovenproof dish with low calorie cooking spray. Spoon half of the mince mixture into the base, top with half of the lasagne sheets and cover with the remaining mince mixture. Add a layer using up the remaining lasagne sheets and spread the yogurt mixture over the top. Sprinkle over the cheese and bake for 25-30 minutes or until golden and the lasagne sheets are soft.

Serve hot with a mixed salad.

chilli con carne

serves 4

Free

ready in 45 minutes

---

low calorie cooking spray

1 large onion, finely chopped

3 garlic cloves, finely chopped

2 tsp ground cumin

1 tsp ground coriander

½ tsp ground cinnamon

1-2 tsp cayenne pepper or smoked paprika

500g lean beef mince (5% fat or less)

400g can chopped tomatoes

1 red pepper and 1 yellow pepper, deseeded and roughly chopped

salt and freshly ground black pepper

400g can red kidney beans in chilli sauce

400g can mixed pulses, drained

small handful of roughly chopped fresh coriander, to garnish

lime wedges, to serve

Our take on the Tex-Mex campfire classic is packed with filling beef and beans, infused with smoky spices and completely Free!

Spray a large non-stick frying pan with low calorie cooking spray and place over a medium heat. Add the onion and garlic and stir-fry for 1-2 minutes, then add the spices and beef and stir-fry for 5-6 minutes.

Add the tomatoes and peppers and bring to the boil over a high heat. Season to taste, cover and cook over a low heat for 20 minutes. Stir in the beans and pulses and cook for a further 10 minutes.

Divide the chilli between bowls, scatter over the coriander and serve hot with lime wedges and rice.

Chilli con carne also makes a terrific topping for jacket potatoes.

individual
lancashire hotpots

serves 4

1 Syn per serving

ready in 2 hours 15 minutes

It's the sliced potato topping that makes this regional favourite such a treat. We've used individual dishes for an extra touch of luxury.

750g potatoes, peeled and thinly sliced

1 tbsp chopped fresh thyme leaves, plus sprigs to garnish

salt and freshly ground black pepper

900g lean lamb leg steaks, visible fat removed, cut into bite-sized chunks

2 large onions, thinly sliced

2 large carrots, peeled and thinly sliced

600ml boiling lamb or beef stock

1 level tbsp lamb or beef gravy granules

Preheat the oven to 180°C/Fan 160°C/Gas 4 and line four individual casserole dishes (or one large dish) with half of the potatoes. Scatter half of the thyme and season to taste.

Layer the lamb, onions and carrots on top of the potatoes, scattering the remaining thyme as you go. Finish with a neat layer of overlapping potato slices.

Mix the stock with the gravy granules and pour enough into the dishes to reach the bottom of the top layer of potatoes. Season to taste.

Cover the dishes with foil and bake for 1½ hours, then uncover and cook for 15-20 minutes or until the potatoes are brown and crisp and the meat is tender.

Garnish with thyme sprigs and serve hot with salad.

lamb saag

If you like spicy food you'll adore this much-loved Indian dish. Tender lamb and fresh spinach are a match made in curry heaven!

serves 4

Free

❄ *SP*

ready in 1 hour

Preheat the oven to 180°C/Fan 160°C/Gas 4.

Put all of the ingredients except the spinach in a lidded casserole pan, season to taste and stir to combine.

Bring to the boil over a high heat, cover the pan and transfer to the oven. Cook for 30 minutes then stir in the spinach and cook for another 15-20 minutes or until the sauce has thickened and the meat is tender.

Divide between shallow bowls, scatter over the extra chilli and serve hot with lime wedges to squeeze over.

Save money by using frozen spinach instead, if you prefer.

700g lean lamb leg steaks, visible fat removed, cut into bite-sized chunks

2 onions, finely chopped

3 garlic cloves, finely chopped

4cm piece of root ginger, peeled and finely grated

1 red chilli, deseeded and finely chopped, plus extra to garnish

4 tbsp curry powder (heat level to your taste)

750ml boiling lamb or chicken stock

1 cinnamon stick

2 cardamom pods, crushed

400g baby spinach leaves, roughly chopped

salt and freshly ground black pepper

lime wedges, to serve

sweet and sour pork

serves 4

1 Syn per serving

ready in 40 minutes

---

low calorie cooking spray

500g lean pork fillet, visible
fat removed, cut into chunks

1 large onion, cut into chunks

1 red pepper, deseeded
and cut into chunks

1 yellow pepper, deseeded
and cut into chunks

2 carrots, peeled and cut
into matchsticks

50g fresh bean sprouts, rinsed

200g sugar snap peas

150g prepared fresh
pineapple, cut into chunks

for the sauce

200ml boiling chicken stock

2 garlic cloves, crushed

1 level tbsp cornflour

1 tbsp tomato purée

2 tbsp white wine vinegar

4 tbsp dark soy sauce

Your tastebuds will love the contrast of sweet
pineapple and the sour notes of vinegar and soy
sauce in our low-Syn version of the classic takeaway.

Spray a non-stick wok or large frying pan with low calorie cooking spray
and place over a high heat. Add the pork and stir-fry for 5-6 minutes or
until lightly browned. Transfer the pork to a bowl with a slotted spoon,
cover and keep warm.

Put all the vegetables into the pan and stir-fry for 4-5 minutes.
Return the pork to the pan and stir-fry for 5-6 minutes or until the
meat is cooked through.

Meanwhile, mix all the sauce ingredients in a small bowl.

Stir the sauce and the pineapple into the pork and vegetables and
cook for 3-4 minutes. Serve hot with Thai fragrant/jasmine rice
garnished with shredded spring onions.

roast pork, spuds and apple sauce

serves 4

2½ **Syns** per serving

ready in 1 hour 40 minutes, plus resting

low calorie cooking spray

4 garlic cloves, unpeeled

4 rosemary sprigs, leaves picked

1.5kg pork loin joint, visible fat removed

salt and freshly ground black pepper

1kg floury potatoes such as Maris Piper, peeled and cut into chunks

4 level tsp gravy granules

for the apple sauce

2 large eating apples, peeled, cored and chopped

1 tbsp finely grated unwaxed lemon zest

1 tsp sweetener

Our irresistible low-Syn roast is the ideal way to bring the family together at the weekend – and apple sauce is the perfect partner for pork.

Preheat the oven to 200°C/Fan 180°C/Gas 6.

Spray a roasting tin with low calorie cooking spray, scatter the garlic and half of the rosemary leaves and place the pork on top. Season to taste, cover loosely with foil (to stop the meat drying out) and roast at the top of the oven for 1½ hours or until the pork is cooked through.

Meanwhile, cook the potatoes in lightly salted boiling water for 10 minutes, then drain well and tip into another roasting tin. Spray with low calorie cooking spray, sprinkle over the remaining rosemary and a little salt. When the pork has 20 minutes to go, move it to a lower shelf and roast the potatoes at the top of the oven for 30 minutes.

While the potatoes are roasting, make the apple sauce. Put the apples, zest and sweetener in a pan with 3 tablespoons of water. Cover and cook over a low heat for 20 minutes or until soft and mushy.

Remove the pork from the pan and set aside for 10-15 minutes to rest, draining off any fat. While the pork is resting, make up the gravy granules as instructed.

Slice the pork and serve with the potatoes, gravy, apple sauce and your favourite vegetables.

The apple sauce can be made in advance and either reheated or served at room temperature.

szechuan pork
with noodles

serves 4

Free

ready in 40 minutes

350g dried egg noodles

500g lean pork mince
(5% fat or less)

2 tbsp soy sauce

2 tbsp sherry vinegar or
rice wine vinegar

low calorie cooking spray

2 garlic cloves, crushed

3cm piece of root ginger,
peeled and grated

2 chillies, deseeded and
finely sliced

1 tsp Szechuan
peppercorns, crushed
(or use dried chilli flakes)

half a bunch of spring onions,
sliced diagonally

1 red pepper, deseeded
and sliced

100g baby sweetcorn, sliced

100g asparagus tips, sliced

150ml boiling chicken stock

Food from the Chinese province of Szechuan is known for being hot and garlicky, and this sizzling stir-fry shows it off at its very best.

Cook the noodles according to the packet instructions. Drain and keep warm.

Meanwhile, put the pork, soy sauce and vinegar in a bowl and mix well.

Place a non-stick wok or deep frying pan over a high heat. Add the pork mixture and stir-fry for 8-10 minutes or until browned and cooked through. Drain off any fat in the pan and tip the pork into a bowl.

Wipe the pan, spray with low calorie cooking spray and turn the heat to medium. Add the garlic, ginger, chillies, Szechuan peppercorns, spring onions, red pepper, sweetcorn and asparagus and stir-fry for 3 minutes.

Add the stock and bring to the boil over a high heat. Turn the heat down to medium and simmer for 5 minutes or until reduced and thickened.

Return the pork to the pan and cook for 2-3 minutes then stir in the noodles and serve hot.

perfect pulled pork
with spicy wedges

serves 4

Free

❄

ready in 8½ hours

500g passata

5 tbsp Worcestershire sauce

3 tbsp balsamic vinegar

1 tsp mustard powder

2 garlic cloves, crushed

3 tbsp sweetener

salt and freshly ground black pepper

low calorie cooking spray

1.5-2kg pork shoulder joint, visible fat removed

for the wedges

1kg sweet potatoes, scrubbed or peeled and cut into thick wedges

1 tbsp Cajun seasoning

Ultra-tender pulled meat is such a treat and this unforgettable slow cooker recipe creates succulent pork that just falls off the bone.

Put the passata, Worcestershire sauce, balsamic vinegar, mustard powder, garlic, sweetener and seasoning into a small pan and mix well. Simmer over a low heat for 15 minutes or until the sauce thickens.

Meanwhile, spray a non-stick frying pan with low calorie cooking spray and place over a high heat. Put the pork joint in the pan and sear on all sides, then tip the joint into a slow cooker (or see tip). Pour in the sauce, coating the meat well, and cook for 8-12 hours on medium.

About 45 minutes before you want to eat, preheat the oven to 220°C/Fan 200°C/Gas 7. Put the sweet potato wedges in a roasting tin, scatter over the Cajun seasoning and toss well. Spray with low calorie cooking spray and roast for 30 minutes or until tender.

Remove the pork from the slow cooker and place on a chopping board. Allow the meat to cool for 15 minutes then shred into bite-sized pieces using two forks.

The pulled pork is delicious served hot with the spicy wedges and crunchy coleslaw (see page 142).

If you don't have a slow-cooker, sear the joint in a casserole pan. Pour in the sauce, coat well, cover and cook in an oven preheated to 120°C/Fan 100°C/Gas ½ for 5-6 hours.

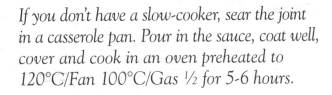

sticky five-spice gammon with pak choi

serves 4

1 Syn per serving

ready in 20 minutes

---

low calorie cooking spray

2 tsp Chinese five-spice powder

4 gammon steaks, visible fat removed, cut into bite-sized chunks

2 red chillies, deseeded and finely chopped

finely grated zest and juice of 1 orange

1 level tbsp clear honey

100ml boiling chicken stock

2 tbsp dark soy sauce

4 pak choi, quartered lengthways

Five-spice is a blend of aromatic spices – typically cloves, fennel seeds, cinnamon, star anise and Szechuan peppercorns – and it really packs a punch in this speedy supper.

Spray a wide non-stick frying pan with low calorie cooking spray and place over a high heat. Sprinkle the five-spice powder over the gammon and cook for 2-3 minutes or until brown at the edges.

Add the chillies, orange zest and juice, honey, stock and soy sauce. Stir well and simmer for 4-5 minutes or until the sauce is sticky and the gammon is glazed and golden.

Meanwhile, steam the pak choi over a pan of boiling water for 5-6 minutes.

Divide the gammon between plates and pour over any juices in the pan. Serve hot with the pak choi and your favourite noodles or rice.

Serve with extra Speed vegetables rather than noodles or rice to make a great Extra Easy **SP** *meal.*

bacon and mushroom
crustless quiche

This comforting quiche is bursting with deliciousness – it's ideal for lunch or served cold for a picnic on a hot summer's day.

Preheat the oven to 190°C/Fan 170°C/Gas 5.

Spray a non-stick frying pan with low calorie cooking spray and place over a medium heat. Add the bacon and fry for 2 minutes then drain off any liquid in the pan. Add the mushrooms and garlic, season to taste and cook for another 4-5 minutes. Spoon the mixture into a 22cm flan dish and spread it out evenly.

Mix the eggs, cottage cheese and most of the parsley in a bowl and spoon the mixture over the bacon and mushrooms.

Push the tomato halves into the top, cut-side up, scatter over the Cheddar and bake for 15-20 minutes or until just set.

Scatter over the remaining parsley and serve warm with salad or your favourite vegetables.

You can leave out the cheese to make this quiche completely Free.

serves 4

1½ Syns per serving

ready in 35 minutes

---

low calorie cooking spray

16 back bacon rashers, visible fat removed, roughly chopped

300g mushrooms, sliced

4 garlic cloves, finely chopped

salt and freshly ground black pepper

6 large eggs, lightly beaten

300g low fat natural cottage cheese

small handful of finely chopped fresh parsley

150g cherry tomatoes, halved

40g reduced fat Cheddar-style cheese, grated

special fried rice

serves 4

Free

ready in 35 minutes

300g dried long-grain rice

low calorie cooking spray

8 back bacon rashers, visible
fat removed, roughly chopped

125g button mushrooms,
sliced or roughly chopped

2 garlic cloves, crushed

5cm piece of root ginger,
peeled and grated

200g green beans,
roughly chopped

1 large carrot, peeled
and diced

150g frozen peas

2 cooked skinless and
boneless chicken breasts,
roughly shredded

200g cooked and peeled
king or tiger prawns,
with or without tails

100g fresh bean sprouts,
rinsed

4 tbsp light soy sauce

2 eggs, lightly beaten

half a bunch of spring onions,
sliced diagonally

lime wedges, to serve

The big brother of egg fried rice is a meal in itself
– and our executive version is packed full of goodies
like prawns, chicken, bacon and mushrooms.

Cook the rice according to the packet instructions then drain, cool
under cold running water and set aside.

Meanwhile, spray a non-stick wok or large frying pan with low calorie
cooking spray and place over a medium heat. Add the bacon,
mushrooms, garlic, ginger, green beans, carrot and peas and stir-fry
for 2-3 minutes.

Turn the heat up to high, stir in the rice, chicken, prawns and bean
sprouts and stir-fry for 2-3 minutes or until piping hot.

Stir in the soy sauce and drizzle over the beaten egg. Stir-fry for another
2-3 minutes or until the egg is cooked and scrambled. Remove from the
heat, scatter over the spring onions and serve hot with lime wedges.

perfect poultry

Chicken and turkey work brilliantly in so many dishes and our classic Food Optimised recipes are so simple you'll never get into a flap in the kitchen!

pizza-topped chicken

serves 4

2½ Syns per serving

ready in 40 minutes

---

low calorie cooking spray

1 red onion, finely chopped

2 red peppers, deseeded and finely chopped

2 garlic cloves, crushed

4 tbsp chicken stock or water

400g can chopped tomatoes

1 tbsp tomato purée

1 tbsp dried oregano

4 skinless and boneless chicken breasts

125g light mozzarella cheese, diced

small handful of finely chopped fresh basil, plus leaves to garnish

This Slimming World favourite offers all the fun of a pizza without the sky-high Syns that come with the dough. Feel free to switch the toppings to other Free favourites!

Preheat the oven to 220°C/Fan 200°C/Gas 7.

Spray a non-stick frying pan with low calorie cooking spray and place over a medium heat. Add the onion, peppers and garlic and cook for 10 minutes, stirring occasionally. Add the stock or water, chopped tomatoes, tomato purée and oregano and simmer for another 15 minutes.

Meanwhile, slice into the side of each chicken breast, being careful not to cut the whole way through, and open them up like butterflies.

Spray another non-stick frying pan with low calorie cooking spray and place over a high heat. Fry the chicken breasts for 1-2 minutes on each side or until they start to colour, then put them in a roasting tin and roast for 15-20 minutes or until cooked through.

Spoon the tomato mixture over the chicken, scatter over the mozzarella and chopped basil and return to the oven for another 5 minutes to melt the cheese.

Scatter over the basil leaves and serve hot with your favourite vegetables.

spicy
chicken salad

serves 4

1½ Syns per serving

ready in 15 minutes,
plus marinating

---

4 skinless and boneless
chicken breasts, sliced thickly

juice of 1 lemon

4 level tbsp tikka curry paste

2 garlic cloves, crushed

200g green beans, trimmed

low calorie cooking spray

small bag of baby leaf spinach

200g cherry tomatoes, halved

150g fat free natural yogurt,
sprinkled with smoked paprika

freshly ground black pepper

This glorious salad is packed with filling chicken, fresh tomatoes and peppery spinach – all spiked with the unmistakable aroma of Indian spices.

Put the chicken in a large bowl and add the lemon juice, curry paste and garlic. Toss well to coat the chicken, cover and marinate in the fridge or a cool place for 30 minutes.

Cook the beans in a pan of lightly salted boiling water for 3-4 minutes or until tender but with a little bite. Drain and keep warm.

Meanwhile, spray a large non-stick frying pan with low calorie cooking spray and place over a medium heat. Tip in the chicken and the marinade and stir-fry for 5-7 minutes or until the chicken is cooked through.

Divide the spinach, beans and tomatoes between plates and top with the chicken. Drizzle over the yogurt and add a good grind of black pepper to serve.

ultimate
chicken casserole

serves 4

Free

ready in 50 minutes

---

low calorie cooking spray

800g skinless and boneless chicken thighs, cut into chunks

2 large onions, roughly chopped

400g baby carrots, halved lengthways

1 whole garlic bulb

700ml boiling chicken stock

salt and freshly ground black pepper

200g green beans, halved

1 lemon, cut into wedges

small handful of finely chopped fresh tarragon, to garnish

This simple stew brings the fabulous flavours of French country cooking to your table – and because it's all in one pot, washing-up will be a breeze.

Spray a large non-stick lidded casserole pan with low calorie cooking spray and place over a high heat. Add the chicken pieces and lightly brown on all sides.

Add the onions, carrots, garlic bulb and stock. Season to taste and bring to the boil. Reduce the heat to medium-low, cover tightly and cook for 25 minutes.

Add the greens beans and lemon wedges and cook for 5-8 minutes.

Discard the garlic bulb, scatter over the tarragon and serve hot.

If you're not eating this as an Extra Easy SP meal, it's delicious with a big bowl of mashed potatoes!

chicken chow mein

serves 4

½ **Syn** per serving

ready in 30 minutes

---

3 tbsp light soy sauce

1 level tbsp hot chilli sauce

2 tsp rice wine vinegar or white wine vinegar

4 garlic cloves, crushed

2cm piece of root ginger, peeled and finely grated

1 tsp Chinese five-spice powder

3 skinless and boneless chicken breasts, thinly sliced

300g dried egg noodles

low calorie cooking spray

200g mangetout, cut into thin strips

225g can water chestnuts, drained and sliced

225g can bamboo shoots, drained

1 red pepper, deseeded and thinly sliced

bunch of spring onions, sliced diagonally

1 level tbsp sweet chilli sauce

3 tbsp dark soy sauce

Serve up this classic Chinese noodle stir-fry and give everyone a takeaway-style treat – or rename it *chow mine* and keep it all for yourself!

Put the light soy sauce, hot chilli sauce, vinegar, garlic, ginger and five-spice powder in a large bowl and mix them all together. Add the chicken and stir to coat well in the dressing. Leave to marinate for 10 minutes.

Meanwhile, cook the noodles according to the packet instructions and drain well.

Spray a large non-stick wok or frying pan with low calorie cooking spray and place over a high heat. Add the chicken mixture and stir-fry for 4-5 minutes or until the chicken is lightly browned.

Add all the vegetables and stir-fry for a further 5 minutes. Add the cooked noodles, sweet chilli sauce and dark soy sauce and cook for 4 minutes or until piping hot.

Serve hot.

chicken tikka masala

It's Britain's number-one takeaway – and this version is one of our members' favourites too.

In a large dish, mix the lime juice, yogurt and 3 tablespoons of the tikka curry powder. Season to taste, add the chicken and toss to coat well. Marinate in the fridge for 4 hours or overnight if you have time.

When you're ready to cook, preheat the grill to medium.

Spray a large non-stick frying pan with low calorie cooking spray and place over a medium heat. Add the onion, garlic, ginger, chilli, cinnamon, cumin and remaining tikka curry powder, stir well and fry for 2-3 minutes. Stir in the tomato purée and 250ml of water. Bring to the boil, reduce the heat to low and simmer for 12-15 minutes, stirring often.

Meanwhile, thread the chicken pieces on to metal skewers, spray with low calorie cooking spray and grill for 12-15 minutes or until cooked through and lightly charred, turning occasionally. Slide the chicken off the skewers and into the sauce, stirring well.

Remove the pan from the heat and stir in the fromage frais. Scatter over the coriander and serve hot with your favourite rice and salad.

serves 4
Free
ready in 45 minutes, plus marinating

juice of 1 lime

150g fat free natural yogurt

5 tbsp tikka curry powder

salt and freshly ground black pepper

4 skinless and boneless chicken breasts, cut into bite-sized chunks

low calorie cooking spray

1 onion, grated

4 garlic cloves, crushed

2cm piece of root ginger, peeled and grated

1 red chilli, deseeded and chopped, plus sliced chilli to garnish

1 tsp ground cinnamon

1 tsp ground cumin

6 tbsp tomato purée

5 tbsp fat free natural fromage frais

small handful of roughly chopped fresh coriander, to garnish

chicken, sweet potato and squash tagine

Tagines are slow-cooked North African stews and this one offers a sensational blend of tastes, colours and aromas.

serves 4

Free

ready in 1 hour 10 minutes

Put the saffron and 2 tablespoons of warm water in a small bowl and set aside.

Spray a deep, non-stick, lidded frying pan with low calorie cooking spray and place over a high heat. Add the chicken and cook for 4-5 minutes, turning to brown on all sides (you might need to do this in batches). Remove the chicken from the pan and set aside.

Add the onions to the pan in a single layer. Mash the garlic with a teaspoon of salt and add to the pan along with the saffron water, ginger, cinnamon, sweet paprika, lemon juice and preserved lemons, if using. Add the parsley and half of the coriander and stir well.

Arrange the chicken thighs, sweet potatoes and squash on top. Pour the stock and passata into the pan and stir well, then cover tightly and simmer over a low heat for 45-50 minutes or until the chicken is cooked through.

Season to taste, scatter over the remaining coriander and serve hot with couscous.

To save time, use two packs of prepared sweet potatoes and butternut squash instead of peeling and chopping them yourself. Most supermarkets stock these ready-to-cook chunks.

pinch of saffron

low calorie cooking spray

8 skinless chicken thighs

2 red onions, halved and thinly sliced

3 garlic cloves, crushed

salt and freshly ground black pepper

2 tsp ground ginger

1 tsp cinnamon

1 tsp sweet smoked paprika

juice of ½ lemon

4 preserved lemons, halved (optional)

small handful of finely chopped fresh parsley

small handful of finely chopped fresh coriander

2 large sweet potatoes, peeled and cut into chunks

½ butternut squash, peeled, deseeded and cut into chunks

500ml boiling chicken stock

200g passata

creamy
chicken pasta

serves 4
Free
ready in 20 minutes

This easy dinner is super-speedy to cook and seriously satisfying, with the creamy sauce adding an indulgent finishing touch.

350g dried pasta shapes, such as fusilli or penne

4 carrots, peeled and cut into batons

bunch of spring onions, finely sliced

1 red pepper, deseeded and cut into strips

150g baby sweetcorn, sliced diagonally

200g sugar snap peas, sliced diagonally

2 cooked skinless and boneless chicken breasts, cut into bite-sized chunks

salt and freshly ground black pepper

small handful of finely chopped fresh chives, to garnish

for the sauce

300g fat free natural fromage frais or quark

1 tsp mustard powder, mixed with 2 tsp water

grated zest and juice of 1 unwaxed lemon

Cook the pasta according to the packet instructions then drain and tip into a large serving bowl.

Meanwhile, put all the vegetables into a saucepan of lightly salted boiling water over a high heat and cook for 5 minutes. Drain and add to the serving bowl along with the chicken.

Put all the ingredients for the sauce in a bowl and whisk until smooth. Tip the sauce into a small pan and heat gently for a few minutes, taking care that it doesn't split.

Stir the sauce into the pasta, season to taste and scatter over the chives to serve.

chicken fajitas with tomato salsa

serves 4 (makes 12)

Free

ready in 30 minutes

---

low calorie cooking spray

1 red pepper, deseeded and finely sliced

1 yellow pepper, deseeded and finely sliced

1 large red onion, halved and finely sliced

1 red chilli, deseeded and finely chopped

juice of 1 lime

1 tsp smoked paprika

1 tsp ground cumin

3 cooked skinless and boneless chicken breasts, shredded

2 Little Gem lettuces, leaves separated

small handful of finely chopped fresh coriander

for the tomato salsa

350g cherry tomatoes

1 red chilli, deseeded

small handful of fresh coriander

juice of 1 lime

salt and freshly ground black pepper

This Tex-Mex treat is a real explosion of flavours, including tender chicken, fresh peppers, hot chilli and mouth-watering spices. We've replaced the usual tortilla wraps with lettuce to make it Free – hurrah!

Spray a non-stick frying pan with low calorie cooking spray and place over a medium-high heat. Add the peppers, onion, chilli, lime juice and spices and fry for 10 minutes, stirring occasionally.

Meanwhile, tip the salsa ingredients into a food processor, season to taste and pulse briefly to chop roughly. Transfer to a bowl.

Tip the chicken and vegetables on to a platter and serve with the lettuce leaves and salsa. Invite everyone to assemble their own fajitas by filling the lettuce leaves with the chicken and vegetables, scattering over the coriander and topping with a spoonful of salsa.

diet cola chicken

If you've never tasted this quirky classic loved by Slimming World members, you're in for a treat. Once you've tried it, you'll be hooked!

Spray a wide non-stick frying pan with low calorie cooking spray and place over a high heat. Add the chicken, peppers and onion and stir-fry for 5 minutes or until lightly browned.

Add the diet cola, stock, passata, tomato purée, garlic, Worcestershire sauce, soy sauce and dried mixed herbs and stir well. Bring to the boil, cover, reduce the heat to medium-low and simmer for 12-15 minutes.

Stir in the sugar snap peas and turn the heat to medium-high. Cook for another 10-15 minutes or until the chicken is cooked through and the veg is tender.

Serve hot with mashed potatoes.

Serve with extra Speed veg rather than mash to make this a great Extra Easy *meal.*

serves 4

Free

❄

ready in 50 minutes

low calorie cooking spray

4 skinless and boneless chicken breasts, cut into chunks

1 red pepper, cut into chunks

1 yellow pepper, cut into chunks

1 green pepper, cut into chunks

1 onion, finely chopped

330ml can diet cola

200ml boiling chicken stock

120g passata with onions and garlic

4 tbsp tomato purée

2 garlic cloves, finely chopped

2 tsp Worcestershire sauce

1 tbsp dark soy sauce

1 tsp dried mixed herbs

200g sugar snap peas

t chilli
chicken

It's the mouth-watering Asian marinade that turns this simple dish into a memorable roast chicken feast.

4 garlic cloves, crushed

2cm piece of root ginger, peeled and grated

100ml soy sauce

2 level tbsp sweet chilli sauce

1 red chilli, deseeded and finely chopped

12 skinless chicken thighs

salt and freshly ground black pepper

small handful of roughly chopped fresh coriander and coriander sprigs (optional), to garnish

lime wedges, to serve

Preheat your oven to 200°C/Fan 180°C/Gas 6.

Put the garlic, ginger, soy sauce, sweet chilli sauce and chilli into a small bowl and mix well. Put the chicken into a shallow dish, pour the soy sauce mixture over the chicken and toss to coat well. (If you have time, cover and leave to marinate in the fridge for 1 hour.)

Arrange the chicken thighs in a single layer in a non-stick roasting tin, season to taste and roast for 30-35 minutes or until cooked through.

Divide the chicken between plates and serve hot with coriander, lime wedges, rice and your favourite vegetables. Garnish with coriander sprigs, if you like.

Serve with your favourite Speed vegetables instead of rice to make a great Extra Easy **SP** *meal.*

chicken kievs

serves 4

1½ Syns per serving

ready in 50 minutes

---

4 skinless and boneless
chicken breasts

salt and freshly ground
black pepper

2 garlic cloves, crushed

2 tbsp low fat natural
cottage cheese

1 tbsp finely chopped fresh
parsley, plus extra to garnish

3 level tbsp freshly grated
Parmesan cheese

1 small egg, beaten

30g wholemeal bread,
crumbed

low calorie cooking spray

This dish was hugely popular in the 1970s but we think the oozy, cheesy, garlicky filling is too tasty to ever go out of fashion!

Preheat the oven to 190°C/Fan 170°C/Gas 5.

Slice into the side of each chicken breast to form a 'pocket', taking care not to cut all the way through. Season the cavity.

In a small bowl, mix the garlic, cottage cheese, parsley and 2 tablespoons of the Parmesan. Spoon the mixture into the chicken cavities and press gently to seal, skewering with a cocktail stick if you need to. Put the chicken on a baking tray lined with non-stick baking parchment.

Brush the bottom of each chicken breast with egg and sprinkle over half of the breadcrumbs. Turn them back over and repeat with more egg and the remaining breadcrumbs. Sprinkle with the remaining Parmesan.

Spray the kievs with low calorie cooking spray and roast for 25-30 minutes or until lightly golden and cooked through.

Scatter over the extra parsley and serve hot with your favourite potatoes and vegetables.

easy
chicken curry

serves 4

Free

ready in 1 hour

---

2 large onions, sliced

600ml boiling chicken stock

3cm piece of root ginger,
peeled and grated

3 garlic cloves, crushed

2 tbsp curry powder
(heat level to your taste)

4 skinless and boneless
chicken breasts,
cut into chunks

275g fat free natural yogurt,
brought to room temperature

salt and freshly ground
black pepper

small handful of finely chopped
fresh coriander, to garnish

This Extra Easy classic is the simplest curry you'll ever make – and quite possibly the tastiest too!

Put the onions and 425ml of stock in a large, heavy-based saucepan. Cover, bring to the boil over a high heat and cook for 10 minutes. Reduce the heat to low, take off the lid and simmer gently for 20 minutes or until the onions are golden and syrupy.

Add the ginger, garlic and curry powder to the pan and cook for 3-4 minutes. Add the chicken and cook for 3 minutes then stir in the remaining stock. Turn the heat to medium, cover and cook for 20 minutes or until the chicken is cooked through.

Take the pan off the heat and stir in the yogurt a little at a time. Season to taste, scatter over the coriander and serve hot with basmati rice.

turkey and broccoli pasta bake

serves 4

1 Syn per serving

ready in 35 minutes

300g dried pasta shapes

250g broccoli florets

2 celery sticks, thinly sliced

400g cooked skinless turkey breast, cut into bite-sized chunks

500g passata with herbs

2 garlic cloves, crushed

salt and freshly ground black pepper

40g wholemeal bread, crumbed

2 tsp dried mixed herbs

Fresh broccoli is fantastic with turkey in this gorgeous bake, and the crunchy breadcrumb topping makes every mouthful a pleasure.

Cook the pasta according to the packet instructions. Drain well and set aside.

Meanwhile, cook the broccoli and celery in a saucepan of lightly salted boiling water for 5 minutes or until the broccoli is just beginning to soften. Drain well and rinse under cold running water, then drain again and set aside.

Preheat the grill to medium-high.

Put the turkey in a saucepan with the passata, garlic, broccoli, celery and pasta and bring to the boil over a high heat. Stir well, turn the heat to medium-low and simmer for 5 minutes. Season to taste.

Pour the turkey mixture into four individual heatproof dishes or one large heatproof dish. Scatter the breadcrumbs and herbs evenly over the tops and grill for 5-6 minutes or until the sauce is bubbling and the crumbs are crisp and golden.

Serve hot with a crisp green salad.

turkey koftë kebabs
with harissa sauce

serves 4
Free

ready in 45 minutes

800g lean turkey mince
(5% fat or less)

1 tsp ground cumin

2 tsp ground coriander

2 tsp sweet smoked paprika,
plus extra to sprinkle

2 garlic cloves, crushed

large handful of finely
chopped fresh mint,
plus extra to garnish

low calorie cooking spray

fat free natural yogurt, to serve

for the harissa sauce

2 garlic cloves, crushed

1 onion, finely chopped

2 x 400g cans
chopped tomatoes

2 tsp harissa spice mix

a pinch of sweetener (optional)

salt and freshly ground
black pepper

Kebabs from the takeaway are loaded with Syns but these beauties use lean turkey mince and fragrant spices to keep them completely Free!

First put all the sauce ingredients into a saucepan and bring to the boil over a high heat. Reduce the heat to low and simmer for 30-40 minutes or until the sauce has thickened, stirring occasionally. Season to taste and keep warm.

Meanwhile, put the turkey, cumin, coriander, paprika, garlic and mint into a bowl. Season to taste and mix well. Divide into 24 portions and, using wet hands, roll each portion into a ball. Thread eight metal skewers with three balls each (or use wooden skewers soaked in water for 20 minutes to stop them burning).

Preheat the grill to medium-high.

Put the skewers on the grill rack, spray with low calorie cooking spray and grill for 6-8 minutes or until lightly browned and cooked through, turning once.

Divide the harissa sauce between plates or shallow bowls and top each one with two koftë skewers. Whisk the yogurt until smooth and drizzle over the koftë, then sprinkle with the extra paprika and mint.

Serve hot with couscous and your favourite vegetables.

The koftë can be made up to 24 hours ahead and kept in the fridge until you're ready to cook.

deep-sea delights

We've cast our net far and wide to find
Slimming World's greatest ever fish feasts.
There's never been a better time to enjoy
the catch of the day!

fish and chips

serves 4

1½ Syns per serving

ready in 45 minutes

Get that Friday feeling with our delicious low-Syn version of the great British takeaway – including our famous Slimming World chips.

low calorie cooking spray

4 skinless and boneless cod fillets

juice of 1 lemon, plus wedges to serve

salt and freshly ground black pepper

1kg floury potatoes such as Maris Piper or King Edward, peeled and cut into thick chips

2 eggs

2 medium slices of bread from a small 400g wholemeal loaf, crumbed

small handful of finely chopped fresh parsley

Preheat the oven to 200°C/Fan 180°C/Gas 6 and spray two non-stick baking sheets with low calorie cooking spray.

Put the cod fillets in a bowl, sprinkle over the lemon juice and season to taste.

Cook the chips in lightly salted boiling water for 5 minutes then drain and dry on kitchen paper. Return the chips to the pan and shake to rough up the edges, then tip them on to one of the baking sheets and spread them out. Spray with low calorie cooking spray, season to taste and cook on the top shelf of the oven for 25-30 minutes.

Meanwhile, lightly beat the eggs in a wide bowl. Mix the breadcrumbs, most of the parsley and some seasoning in another wide bowl. Dip each cod fillet first into the egg and then the breadcrumb mixture to coat evenly and arrange them on the second baking sheet. Put the fish into the oven on the shelf below the chips and cook for 15-20 minutes or until the fish is cooked through.

Scatter the remaining parsley over the fish and serve hot with mushy peas, tartare sauce (see page 106) and lemon wedges to squeeze over.

luxury
fish pie

serves 4

½ **Syn** per serving

ready in 1 hour

---

4 eggs

350ml fish stock

600g skinless and boneless white fish fillets, cut into bite-sized chunks

1 large leek, sliced

200g cooked and peeled king or tiger prawns, tails removed

large handful of chopped fresh dill

small handful of chopped fresh parsley

juice of ½ lemon

2 level tsp cornflour

for the topping

500g carrots, peeled and roughly chopped

500g swede, peeled and roughly chopped

4 tbsp quark

salt and freshly ground black pepper

There's so much going on in this dinner from the deep: fish, prawns, eggs and leek are topped with a comforting carrot and swede mash.

Make the topping first. Put the carrots and swede into a large pan of lightly salted boiling water and cook over a high heat for 25-30 minutes or until tender. Drain, return to the pan and mash. Leave to cool then stir in the quark, season to taste and set aside.

Meanwhile, preheat the oven to 200°C/Fan 180°C/Gas 6.

Put the eggs in a small pan of water and bring to the boil. Reduce the heat to a simmer and cook for 7-8 minutes, until just hard-boiled. Cool under cold running water, peel, quarter and set aside.

Put the stock in a saucepan and bring to a simmer over a medium heat. Add the fish and leek, turn the heat to low and cook for 5 minutes. Using a slotted spoon, transfer the fish and leek to a large, shallow ovenproof dish. Add the prawns, herbs, lemon juice and eggs to the fish and gently mix together.

Strain the fish stock into a clean pan and place over a high heat. Mix the cornflour with 1 tablespoon of cold water and add to the stock. Bring to the boil, reduce the heat to low and cook for 2 minutes. Pour the stock mixture over the fish. Gently mix everything together and season to taste.

Spoon the mash on top, making a pattern with a fork if you're feeling creative! Bake for 20-25 minutes or until the topping is lightly browned.

Serve hot with salad or your favourite vegetables.

haddock fish cakes
with tartare sauce

serves 4
Free

ready in 50 minutes,
plus cooling and chilling

A good fish cake is fantastic comfort food, and these herby heroes go brilliantly with our tasty tartare sauce.

500g potatoes, peeled and quartered

500g skinless and boneless smoked haddock fillet

1 large onion, roughly chopped

small handful of fresh parsley

small handful of fresh dill, plus extra to garnish

2 tbsp fat free natural yogurt

½ tsp cayenne pepper

salt and freshly ground black pepper

2 eggs, beaten

1 large cucumber, shredded, to serve

for the tartare sauce

200g fat free natural yogurt

2 tbsp roughly chopped cocktail gherkins or cornichons

½ red onion, finely chopped

juice of 1 lemon, plus wedges to serve

small handful of finely chopped fresh dill

Cook the potatoes in a saucepan of lightly salted boiling water over a high heat for 12-15 minutes or until tender.

Meanwhile, put the haddock, onion and herbs into a food processor and blitz to chop roughly. Tip into a large bowl and beat in the yogurt, cayenne pepper and seasoning.

Drain and mash the potatoes and add them to the fish along with one beaten egg. Mix together well and divide into eight portions, then shape each one into a ball and flatten into cakes with your hand. Put the cakes on to a baking tray lined with non-stick baking parchment, cool and chill for at least 2 hours (this helps them keep their shape when they are cooked).

Preheat the oven to 200°C/Fan 180°C/Gas 6.

Brush the fish cakes with the remaining egg and bake for 15-20 minutes or until cooked through and lightly brown.

Meanwhile, make the tartare sauce by mixing all the ingredients in a bowl, reserving a little gherkin and onion to sprinkle on top.

Scatter the extra dill over the fish cakes and tartare sauce and serve with the lemon wedges, shredded cucumber and your favourite vegetables.

ginger and soy
salmon with noodles

serves 4

½ **Syn** per serving

ready in 35 minutes

---

4 large skinless and
boneless salmon fillets

6 tbsp dark soy sauce

2cm piece of root ginger,
peeled and finely grated

2 level tsp clear honey

freshly ground black pepper

lime wedges, to serve

for the noodles

low calorie cooking spray

2 garlic cloves, crushed

1cm piece of root ginger,
peeled and grated

1 red chilli, deseeded and
finely chopped

half a bunch of spring onions,
shredded

5 tbsp vegetable stock

2 tbsp dark soy sauce

200g baby sweetcorn,
roughly chopped

2 pak choi, roughly chopped

150g fresh bean
sprouts, rinsed

250g dried rice noodles

Firm, meaty salmon is fantastic with this Asian-style marinade of soy sauce, ginger and honey, and the noodles are packed with Speed veg!

Preheat the grill to medium-high.

Put the salmon fillets in a shallow dish. Mix the soy sauce, ginger and honey, pour over the fish and toss to coat well. Put the salmon on the grill rack, season with black pepper and grill for 12-15 minutes or until cooked through.

While the salmon is cooking, make the noodles. Spray a non-stick wok or large frying pan with low calorie cooking spray and place over a medium heat. Add the garlic, ginger, chilli, spring onions, stock and soy sauce and stir-fry gently for 4-5 minutes.

Turn the heat to high and add the baby sweetcorn, pak choi and bean sprouts. Stir-fry for another 4-5 minutes or until the vegetables are just tender.

Meanwhile, cook the noodles according to the packet instructions and drain well. Add the noodles to the vegetables in the pan. Stir-fry for 1-2 minutes or until everything is piping hot.

Divide the noodles between plates or shallow bowls, top with a salmon fillet and serve hot, with lime wedges to squeeze over.

smoked salmon and potato salad

Embrace the flavours of Scandinavia in this punchy salad combining the smoky flavour of salmon and the bite of capers and gherkins.

serves 4

1 Syn per serving

ready in 20 minutes, plus cooling

Cook the potatoes in a large saucepan of lightly salted boiling water for 12-15 minutes or until just tender. Drain, tip into a serving bowl and leave to cool for 5-10 minutes.

Add the smoked salmon, capers, cornichons or cocktail gherkins, spring onions, lettuce leaves and tomatoes and toss well. Grind over plenty of black pepper.

Whisk the dressing ingredients together, season to taste and serve with the salad.

750g waxy potatoes such as Charlotte, halved

300g smoked salmon, cut into thick strips

2 tbsp capers, drained

100g cocktail gherkins or cornichons, drained and chopped

6 spring onions, thinly sliced

2 Baby Gem lettuces, leaves separated and roughly chopped

200g red and yellow cherry tomatoes, halved

salt and freshly ground black pepper

for the dressing

4 level tbsp extra-light mayonnaise

150g fat free natural yogurt

1 tsp mustard powder mixed with 1 tsp water

small handful of finely chopped fresh dill

juice of 1 lemon

cheesy tuna pasta bake

serves 4

3 Syns per serving

ready in 30 minutes

350g dried pasta shapes

1 leek, trimmed and
thinly sliced

100g frozen spinach

100g frozen sweetcorn

250g quark

175g fat free natural
fromage frais

400g can tuna chunks in brine
or spring water, drained

75g reduced fat Cheddar-style
cheese, grated

salt and freshly ground
black pepper

Pasta bakes are so easy to make and so satisfying – and this one is a real Slimming World family favourite.

Preheat your grill to high.

Cook the pasta according to the packet instructions, reducing the recommended cooking time by 2 minutes. Add the leek, spinach and sweetcorn for the last 4 minutes of the cooking time. Drain the pasta and vegetables and tip them back into the same pan.

Stir in the quark, fromage frais, tuna and half the cheese. Season to taste and tip everything into a heatproof dish that will fit under your grill. Scatter over the remaining cheese and grill for 10 minutes.

Serve hot with salad or your favourite vegetables.

Leave out the cheese to make this tasty bake completely Free!

seafood paella

There are many versions of the classic Spanish rice dish but the seafood kind is probably the most popular – and our version is completely Free!

Spray a large non-stick frying pan or paella pan with low calorie cooking spray and place over a medium-low heat. Add the onion and garlic and stir-fry 4-5 minutes or until softened.

Stir the saffron and turmeric into the chicken stock, then add the stock to the pan and stir in the paprika. Bring to a simmer then add the rice and carrots. Stir once, then cover and leave to simmer gently for 15-20 minutes.

Add the prawns and mixed seafood, red peppers, asparagus, peas and runner beans. Cook for 10 minutes, stirring occasionally, until the rice is soft but not mushy, the vegetables are tender and the seafood is warmed through.

Season to taste, stir in the parsley and serve hot with lemon wedges to squeeze over.

serves 4-6

Free

ready in 40 minutes

___

low calorie cooking spray

1 onion, finely chopped

2 garlic cloves, finely chopped

pinch of saffron

¼ tsp turmeric

900ml boiling chicken stock

1 tbsp smoked paprika

225g dried paella rice

2 large carrots, peeled and diced

8 cooked king prawns, shells left on and heads removed

2 x 225g packs seafood selection (eg squid, mussels and prawns)

2 bottled roasted red peppers in brine, drained and roughly chopped

200g asparagus tips

100g frozen peas

200g runner beans, roughly chopped

salt and freshly ground black pepper

small handful of finely chopped fresh parsley

lemon wedges, to serve

prawn, chilli and tomato linguine

serves 4

Free

ready in 15 minutes

400g dried linguine pasta

low calorie cooking spray

2 garlic cloves, thinly sliced

1-2 red chillies, deseeded and finely chopped

bunch of spring onions, sliced

4 plum tomatoes, deseeded and finely chopped

450g raw peeled king or tiger prawns, with or without tails

small bag of rocket leaves, roughly chopped

salt and freshly ground black pepper

Plump pink prawns are the stars in this elegant pasta dish that's ready in the time it takes to cook the pasta.

Cook the linguine according to the packet instructions, then drain and tip it back into the saucepan.

Meanwhile, spray a non-stick frying pan with low calorie cooking spray and place over a medium-high heat. Add the garlic, most of the chillies and most of the spring onions and stir-fry for 1-2 minutes.

Add the tomatoes and fry for 2-3 minutes then stir in the prawns and fry for another 2-3 minutes or until the prawns are cooked through.

Stir the tomatoes, prawns and rocket into the linguine and divide between bowls. Season to taste, scatter over the remaining chilli and spring onions and serve hot.

prawn biryani

This popular rice dish originally came from Iran but nowadays it's one of the most popular options on Indian restaurant menus. Our recipe is infused with smoky spices and plenty of plump prawns.

Put the onion and stock into a deep non-stick frying pan over a medium heat, stir well and cook for 5-6 minutes or until the onion has softened.

Stir in the garlic, ginger and all the spices and cook for 2-3 minutes.

Add the carrots and green beans and cook for 2-3 minutes, then add the rice and stir-fry for another 2-3 minutes. Season to taste, add 500ml of boiling water and bring to the boil.

Add the prawns, cover tightly and reduce the heat to very low. Cook undisturbed for 12-15 minutes then remove from the heat and leave to stand with the lid on, undisturbed, for 10 minutes or until the water has been completely absorbed.

Fluff up the rice with a fork, scatter over the coriander and serve with the yogurt.

serves 4
Free
ready in 35 minutes,
plus standing

1 onion, finely chopped

200ml boiling vegetable stock

2 garlic cloves, crushed

1cm piece of root ginger, peeled and finely grated

½ tsp dried chilli flakes

½ tsp crushed cardamom seeds

2 tsp cumin seeds

½ tsp turmeric

1 tbsp mild curry powder

1 cinnamon stick

2 cloves

2 carrots, peeled and cut into batons

200g green beans, trimmed and chopped

275g dried basmati rice

salt and freshly ground black pepper

450g raw peeled king or tiger prawns, with or without tails

small handful of chopped fresh coriander, to garnish

fat free natural yogurt sprinkled with coriander and chilli powder or paprika, to serve

VIP veg

Enjoy some meat-free magic with our vibrant veggie mains, perfect pasta sauces and essential sides including coleslaw, pilau rice and chips with curry sauce.

deluxe
mac 'n' cheese

serves 4

3 Syns per serving

ready in 50 minutes

Our Food Optimised version of the much-loved American pasta dish is destined to be a dinner time regular in your home.

400g dried macaroni or other small pasta shapes

low calorie cooking spray

2 leeks, sliced

2 courgettes, sliced

125g mushrooms, sliced

1 tbsp finely chopped fresh parsley, to garnish

for the sauce

2 level tbsp cornflour

250ml skimmed milk

150g fat free natural fromage frais

1 tsp mustard powder, mixed with 2 tsp water

pinch of grated nutmeg

salt and freshly ground black pepper

40g reduced fat Cheddar-style cheese, grated

Preheat the oven to 180°C/Fan 160°C/Gas 4.

Cook the pasta according to the packet instructions then drain well and set aside.

Meanwhile, spray a large non-stick frying pan with low calorie cooking spray and place over a low heat. Add the leeks, courgettes and mushrooms and cook for 8-10 minutes or until softened.

While the vegetables are cooking, make the sauce. Blend the cornflour with a little milk and set aside. Bring the remaining milk to the boil in a saucepan over a medium-high heat, then stir in the cornflour mixture and cook for 1-2 minutes or until thickened, stirring continuously. Remove the pan from the heat and beat in the fromage frais, mustard and nutmeg with a wooden spoon. Season to taste and stir in most of the cheese.

Tip the pasta and vegetables into an ovenproof dish, mix well and pour the sauce over the top. Sprinkle over the rest of the cheese and bake for 20-30 minutes or until crisp and golden.

Scatter over the parsley and serve hot with salad or your favourite vegetables.

asparagus, pea and mint risotto

serves 4

1 Syn per serving

ready in 40 minutes

The vibrant green vegetables and herbs in this soothing low-Syn risotto make it a perfect choice for summer.

1.5 litres boiling vegetable stock

low calorie cooking spray

1 onion, finely chopped

2 garlic cloves, crushed

350g dried arborio rice

200g asparagus tips, halved

200g frozen peas

large handful of shredded fresh mint, plus mint leaves to garnish

4 level tbsp freshly grated Parmesan cheese or vegetarian alternative

Pour the stock into a saucepan over a low heat and leave it to simmer gently.

Spray a heavy-based, non-stick saucepan with low calorie cooking spray and place over a medium heat. Add the onion and cook for 10 minutes or until softened. Add the garlic and rice and stir-fry for 1 minute to coat the rice well. Stir in the asparagus and peas.

Add a couple of ladlefuls of the hot stock and cook until the stock is absorbed, stirring continuously. Continue adding stock, cooking and stirring in this way for 20-25 minutes or until the rice is just cooked.

Remove the risotto from the heat, stir in the shredded mint and leave to rest for 1 minute. Scatter over the cheese and mint leaves to serve.

carrot, pepper and pea dhal

serves 4

Free

ready in 50 minutes

Fabulously filling and Free, lentils go brilliantly with so many ingredients and this popular Indian comfort food hits all the right notes.

low calorie cooking spray

2 onions, finely chopped

4 garlic cloves, finely chopped

1cm piece of root ginger, peeled and finely grated

1 tbsp cumin seeds

1 tbsp black mustard seeds

1 tsp turmeric

2 tbsp mild or medium curry powder

175g dried red split lentils, washed and drained

3 carrots, peeled and cubed

1 red pepper, deseeded and roughly chopped

1 yellow pepper, deseeded and roughly chopped

200g frozen peas

salt

small handful of finely chopped fresh coriander

lime wedges, to serve

Spray a lidded saucepan with low calorie cooking spray and place over a medium heat. Add the onions and stir-fry for 4-5 minutes.

Turn the heat to low and stir in the garlic, ginger and all the spices. Stir-fry for 1-2 minutes then add the lentils and 800ml of water and bring to the boil over a high heat.

Add the carrots, cover and turn the heat to low. Simmer gently for 15-20 minutes or until the mixture is thick, stirring occasionally. Stir in the peppers, cover and cook for 10-12 minutes or until tender.

Stir in the peas, bring back to the boil over a high heat and cook for 2-3 minutes. Season with salt, remove from the heat and stir in the coriander. This is delicious served hot with rice and a squeeze of fresh lime juice.

cauliflower rice pilaf

Cauliflower rice is a big hit with our members – we've used it here to give a twist to a classic Middle Eastern pilaf.

Put the cauliflower into a food processor and pulse until it breaks down and looks like rice.

Tip the cauliflower into a steamer basket and steam over a pan of boiling water for 10-12 minutes or until tender (see tip).

Spray a large non-stick frying pan with low calorie cooking spray and place over a high heat. Add the cumin seeds and mustard seeds and stir-fry for 30 seconds. Add the spring onions and stir-fry for 1-2 minutes. Stir in the cauliflower and stir-fry for 2-3 minutes or until piping hot.

Remove from the heat and stir in the lime juice, cucumber, tomatoes and coriander. Season to taste, toss well and serve hot.

If you don't have a steamer basket, put the cauliflower in a metal colander or sieve and rest it over a large pan of boiling water for 10-12 minutes. You can also cook it in the microwave for 5-6 minutes.

serves 4

Free

ready in 30 minutes

1 large cauliflower, roughly chopped

low calorie cooking spray

2 tsp cumin seeds

1 tsp black mustard seeds

6 spring onions, finely sliced

juice of ½ lime

½ cucumber, halved lengthways, deseeded and finely chopped

200g red and yellow cherry tomatoes, halved or quartered

large handful of finely chopped fresh coriander

salt and freshly ground black pepper

red onion and pepper tortilla

serves 4

Free

ready in 40 minutes

Spain's answer to omelettes and frittatas, tortillas are so satisfying thanks to the potatoes and they're a great option for a light dinner or easy lunch.

low calorie cooking spray

1 red onion, sliced

1 red pepper, deseeded and sliced

1 yellow or orange pepper, deseeded and sliced

2 potatoes, peeled and cubed

2 garlic cloves, finely chopped

1 tsp sweet smoked paprika

6 eggs, lightly beaten

small handful of finely chopped fresh parsley

salt and freshly ground black pepper

Spray a non-stick frying pan with low calorie cooking spray and place over a medium heat. Add the onion, peppers and potatoes and cook for 12-15 minutes or until softened, stirring often. Stir in the garlic and paprika and cook for another minute.

Mix the eggs and most of the parsley together and season to taste. Pour the eggs over the vegetables in the pan, tilting it around to spread the egg evenly. Cook gently for 8-10 minutes or until the tortilla is set at the bottom (you can lift it at the edges with a fish slice to check).

Meanwhile, preheat the grill to medium-hot.

Finish the tortilla under the grill for 3-4 minutes or until the top is golden and set to your liking. Remove from the heat and leave to cool slightly. Scatter over the remaining parsley, cut into wedges and serve with salad.

mushroom and tomato pasta

Mushrooms add a lovely depth of flavour to this simple and very speedy supper.

Spray a non-stick frying pan with low calorie cooking spray and place over a medium heat. Add the mushrooms and stir-fry for 3-4 minutes, then add the garlic and onion and fry for 2-3 minutes. Pour in the tomatoes and bring to the boil, then reduce the heat to low and simmer gently for 10-12 minutes.

While the sauce is simmering, cook the pasta according to the packet instructions. Drain and keep warm.

Remove the sauce from the heat, stir in the fromage frais and season to taste. Stir the sauce into the pasta, scatter over the basil and serve hot.

serves 4

Free

ready in 20 minutes

---

low calorie cooking spray

200g closed-cup mushrooms, sliced

2 garlic cloves, crushed

1 onion, finely chopped

400g can chopped tomatoes

400g dried pasta shapes

150g fat free natural fromage frais

salt and freshly ground black pepper

fresh basil leaves, to garnish

courgette, pepper and feta couscous

serves 4

2 Syns per serving

ready in 35 minutes

2 large courgettes, cubed

1 red pepper, deseeded and cut into chunks

1 yellow pepper, deseeded and cut into chunks

2 red onions, cut into wedges

4 garlic cloves, finely chopped

1 tbsp harissa powder

low calorie cooking spray

350g dried couscous

80g reduced fat feta cheese, diced

small handful of roughly chopped fresh mint, to garnish

salt and freshly ground black pepper

This sensational salad of roasted Mediterranean vegetables, couscous and feta makes a marvellous meal in warmer weather.

Preheat the oven to 200°C/Fan 180°C/Gas 6.

Put the courgettes, peppers and onions in a large roasting tin and sprinkle over the garlic and harissa powder. Spray lightly with low calorie cooking spray, toss well and roast for 20-25 minutes or until tender.

Meanwhile, put the couscous into a heatproof bowl and pour in enough boiling water to just cover. Leave for 10 minutes until the water has been absorbed then fluff up the grains with a fork.

Tip the couscous into a serving dish and stir in the roasted vegetables. To serve, scatter over the feta and mint and season to taste.

hasselback potatoes

It's time to give your roasties a Slimming World makeover! Slicing into the spuds before roasting makes them extra crispy.

Preheat the oven to 200°C/Fan 180°C/Gas 6.

Cut small slices into each potato at regular intervals, taking care not to cut all the way through. Arrange the potatoes on a baking sheet and spray with low calorie cooking spray. Tuck the rosemary sprigs into some of the cuts, sprinkle with sea salt and roast for 10 minutes. Turn the potatoes and cook for a further 30-40 minutes or until cooked through.

serves 4
Free
❄ Ⓥ
ready in 1 hour

1kg small potatoes

low calorie cooking spray

rosemary sprigs

sea salt

best-ever pesto

serves 6 (makes about 450g)

1½ Syns per serving

Ⓥ (if the cheese is vegetarian)

ready in 10 minutes

100g fresh basil leaves

45g freshly grated Parmesan cheese or vegetarian alternative

2 garlic cloves, crushed

2 tsp finely grated unwaxed lemon zest

200g quark

100ml vegetable stock, cooled

salt and freshly ground black pepper

Typical pesto is 3½ Syns per level tablespoon. Our low-Syn version is *just* as delicious – and *so* easy to make.

Put all the ingredients into a food processor, season to taste and blend until smooth. Add a little more stock if you want a looser pesto.

Stir the pesto into your favourite pasta or toss it through vegetables such as potatoes, green beans or asparagus.

The pesto will keep for up to 3 days in the fridge. Try using half basil and half rocket leaves for a more peppery pesto.

slimming world chips with curry sauce

serves 4

Free

ready in 45 minutes

1kg floury potatoes, such as Maris Piper or King Edward, peeled and cut into thick chips

low calorie cooking spray

sea salt

for the curry sauce

1 onion, roughly chopped

2 garlic cloves, crushed

1cm piece of root ginger, peeled and finely grated

1 tbsp curry powder (heat level to your taste)

400g can chopped tomatoes

4 tbsp vegetable stock

2 tbsp sweetener

small handful of fresh coriander and mint

3 tbsp fat free natural fromage frais

There's only one thing better than a big portion of chips… and that's a big portion of chips with a delicious sauce on the side!

Preheat the oven to 200°C/Fan 180°C/Gas 6.

Cook the chips in a large saucepan of lightly salted boiling water over a high heat for 5 minutes. Drain, return to the saucepan and shake to rough up the edges.

Spray a baking sheet with low calorie cooking spray. Transfer the chips to the tray, spray lightly with low calorie cooking spray and cook in the oven for 20-25 minutes or until golden brown on all sides, turning occasionally.

While the chips are cooking, make the curry sauce. Spray a non-stick pan with low calorie cooking spray and place over a medium heat. Add the onion and garlic and cook for 10 minutes or until soft. Add the ginger and cook for 1-2 minutes, then add the curry powder and cook for another 1-2 minutes. Add the tomatoes, stock and sweetener and bring to the boil over a high heat. Reduce the heat to low and simmer for 12-15 minutes.

Transfer the sauce to a food processor, add the herbs and blend until smooth. Return to the pan, stir in the fromage frais and gently heat through (take care not to let it boil or the fromage frais will curdle).

Sprinkle the chips with sea salt and serve hot with the curry sauce.

crunchy coleslaw

serves 4

1 Syn per serving

ready in 15 minutes

___

2 carrots, peeled and coarsely grated

½ white cabbage, finely shredded

4 level tbsp extra-light mayonnaise

juice of 1 lemon

2 tbsp quark

salt and freshly ground black pepper

Cabbage and carrots have never had it so good! This irresistible side dish is fantastic with chicken, pork or ham.

Put the carrots, cabbage, mayonnaise, lemon juice and quark in a large bowl.

Stir well and season to taste, then cover and chill until needed.

roasted
mediterranean veg

serves 4

Free

Ⓥ 𝓢𝓟

ready in 40 minutes

1 large aubergine,
cut into chunks

2 courgettes, cut into chunks

4 tomatoes, halved

1 red onion, cut into wedges

8 garlic cloves, unpeeled

low calorie cooking spray

salt and freshly ground
black pepper

small handful of roughly
chopped fresh parsley,
to garnish

lemon wedges, to serve

Roasting aubergines, courgettes, tomatoes and onions intensifies their deliciousness! Serve this mouth-watering medley as a veggie main meal with rice or as a side dish with grilled meat or fish.

Preheat the oven to 200°C/Fan 180°C/Gas 6.

Put the aubergine, courgettes, tomatoes, onion and garlic into a non-stick roasting tin (you might need to use two tins). Spray with low calorie cooking spray and roast for 20-25 minutes or until tender.

Season to taste, scatter over the parsley and serve hot, with lemon wedges to squeeze over.

pilau rice

350g dried basmati rice

low calorie cooking spray

1 onion, roughly chopped

6 cardamom pods

8 cloves

6 peppercorns

1 cinnamon stick

1 tsp cumin seeds

a small pinch of saffron
(or ½ tsp turmeric)

2 bay leaves

500ml boiling vegetable
stock or water

salt

small handful of finely
chopped fresh coriander,
to garnish

Our Free version of the essential Indian rice is infused with the fragrances of cardamom, cloves and cinnamon.

Soak the rice in cold water then drain in a sieve and rinse under cold running water.

Spray a non-stick lidded saucepan with low calorie cooking spray and place over a medium heat. Add the onion and cook for about 5 minutes or until slightly softened. Add the spices and bay leaves and cook for a further 2 minutes.

Drain the rice, add to the pan and stir until the grains are coated in the spice mixture. Stir in the stock or water, season with salt and bring to the boil.

Cover, turn the heat to low and cook for 10 minutes before turning off the heat. Keep the lid on and leave the rice, undisturbed, for about 10 minutes.

Fluff up the grains, scatter over the coriander and serve hot with your favourite curry.

If you don't like whole spices in your pilau rice, use 2 tablespoons of pilau rice seasoning instead.

roasted winter veg

serves 4

Free

ready in 1 hour

Root vegetables love a bit of time in the oven. Try these as a veggie main course or a colourful accompaniment to a roast.

1 swede, peeled and cut into batons

2 carrots, peeled and cut into batons

4 parsnips, peeled and cut into batons

1 celeriac, peeled and cut into batons

2 red onions, cut into wedges

2 leeks, trimmed and cut into chunks

2 sweet potatoes, peeled and cut into batons

2 garlic cloves, crushed

a few fresh rosemary sprigs (or 1 tbsp dried rosemary), plus extra to garnish

1 tsp coriander seeds, crushed

salt and freshly ground black pepper

low calorie cooking spray

Preheat the oven to 200°C/Fan 180°C/Gas 6.

Put all the vegetables into two non-stick roasting tins and sprinkle over the garlic, rosemary and coriander seeds. Season to taste, spray with low calorie cooking spray and toss the vegetables well.

Roast for 35-40 minutes or until the vegetables are tender and slightly charred. Garnish with rosemary sprigs to serve.

(extra) easy
arrabiata sauce

serves 4

Free

ready in 30 minutes

---

low calorie cooking spray

1 onion, finely chopped

2 red chillies, deseeded and finely chopped

2 garlic cloves, crushed

400g passata

200ml boiling vegetable stock

salt and freshly ground black pepper

fresh basil leaves, to garnish

This fiery and very versatile tomato sauce is usually stirred into pasta but it's just as good served with roasted vegetables, meat or chicken. Adjust the chillies to suit your taste.

Spray a large non-stick frying pan with low calorie cooking spray and place over a medium heat. Add the onion, chillies and garlic and cook for 5 minutes or until slightly softened.

Add the passata and stock to the pan and bring to the boil. Cover, turn the heat to low and simmer for 15-20 minutes or until slightly reduced and thickened. Season to taste.

This sauce is delicious stirred through pasta, roasted vegetables, meat or chicken. Scatter over the basil to serve.

divine desserts

Make way for the sweet trolley! Our selection of classic low-Syn sensations is the perfect way to finish any meal.

raspberry and white chocolate pavlova

serves 8

4½ Syns per serving

ready in 1 hour 50 minutes, plus cooling

4 egg whites

pinch of salt

150g caster sugar

1 level tsp cornflour

1 tsp white wine vinegar or malt vinegar

¼ tsp vanilla extract

25g white chocolate

250g quark

175g pot Muller Light Vanilla yogurt (or any Free vanilla yogurt)

300g raspberries

This wonderful meringue dessert was named in honour of the Russian ballerina, Anna Pavlova, so it's fitting that it's lighter than air!

Preheat your oven to 160°C/Fan 140°C/Gas 3. Draw a circle 20cm across on a sheet of non-stick baking parchment and put it on a baking tray.

Whisk the egg whites and salt with an electric beater until stiff peaks form. Whisk in the caster sugar 1 tablespoon at a time until you have a stiff, glossy mixture. Fold in the cornflour, vinegar and vanilla extract.

Spoon the mixture into the circle drawn on the baking parchment, put the tray in the oven and immediately reduce the heat to 140°C/Fan 120°C/Gas 1. Bake for 1½ hours or until the meringue is crisp to the touch.

Leave to cool, then peel off the baking parchment and put the meringue on a serving plate.

Put the white chocolate in a heatproof bowl over a pan of simmering water and leave to melt without stirring. Cool slightly.

Beat the quark and yogurt together and spoon the mixture on to the meringue. Top with the raspberries and drizzle over the melted white chocolate to serve.

weetabix cake

makes 12 slices

3½ Syns per slice

ready in 1 hour 10 minutes,
plus cooling

---

2 Weetabix

200ml skimmed milk

100g sultanas

100g self-raising flour

1 tsp mixed spice

2 tbsp sweetener

2 large eggs, beaten

This more-ish Slimming World classic tastes a little bit like bread and butter pudding but with the Syns slashed!

Preheat the oven to 180°C/Fan 160°C/Gas 4 and line a 450g loaf tin with non-stick baking parchment.

Put the Weetabix into a large bowl and pour in the milk. Leave for 2-3 minutes then mash with a fork.

Beat in all the remaining ingredients, spoon the mixture into the prepared loaf tin and bake for 1 hour.

Cool the cake on a wire rack, turn out and slice into 12 to serve.

lemon filo tarts

makes 6

3 Syns per tart

ready in 30 minutes

150g quark

grated zest of
½ unwaxed lemon,
plus extra to decorate

a large pinch of sweetener

2 level tbsp lemon curd

low calorie cooking spray

2 x 45g filo pastry sheets

1 level tsp icing sugar, to dust

As you bite into these stunning filo tarts filled with gorgeous lemony quark, you won't believe they're just 3 Syns each!

Preheat your oven to 180°C/Fan 160°C/Gas 4.

Put the quark, lemon zest, sweetener and lemon curd in a bowl, stir lightly and chill until needed.

Spray a medium-sized six-hole muffin tin with low calorie cooking spray.

Cut the pastry sheets into 18 square-ish pieces that are big enough to fit into the muffin holes and lightly spray the pieces with low calorie cooking spray. Stack three pieces on top of each other at different angles and press into a muffin tin hole. Repeat to line all six holes then bake for 5-6 minutes or until crisp and golden. Set aside to cool.

When you're ready to eat, turn out the filo cases and spoon in the lemon mixture. Decorate with the extra lemon zest and dust lightly with icing sugar to serve. For best results, eat straight away while the filo is crisp.

banoffee pie

This celebrated pie was created in Britain in the 1970s, and the combination of banana and toffee has been thrilling pudding fans ever since. Our version uses toffee yogurt and fresh bananas to keep the Syns ultra low!

Preheat the oven to 190°C/Fan 170°C/Gas 5 and line a 20cm springform tin with non-stick baking parchment.

Melt the spread in a pan over a low heat.

Meanwhile, put the biscuits in a sealable food bag, bash into fine crumbs with a rolling pin and tip into a bowl. Pour in the melted spread, stir well and spoon the mixture into the prepared tin to cover the base, pressing down evenly. Bake for 12-15 minutes then set aside to cool.

While the base is in the oven, put 150ml of hot (but not boiling) water in a shallow dish, sprinkle over the gelatine powder and stir to dissolve.

Put the quark in a bowl and whisk until smooth, then whisk in the yogurt, sweetener, vanilla and gelatine liquid.

Whisk the egg whites in a bowl until stiff peaks form and fold into the quark mixture.

Spoon the quark mixture over the biscuit base and smooth the surface with a palette knife. Chill for 4 hours or until set.

Release the pie from the tin and put the pie, still on its base if necessary, on a serving plate. Thinly slice the bananas and arrange neatly on top, then sprinkle with cocoa powder and slice to serve.

serves 10

4 Syns per serving

ready in 30 minutes, plus cooling and setting

60g low fat spread

10 reduced fat digestive biscuits

2 x 12g sachets powdered gelatine

250g quark

3 x 175g pots Muller Light Toffee yogurt (or any Free toffee yogurt)

1 tbsp sweetener

1 tsp vanilla extract

2 egg whites*

2 bananas

2 level tsp cocoa powder, to decorate

*Pregnant women, the elderly and babies are advised not to eat raw or partially cooked eggs.

summer fruits terrine

serves 4

½ **Syn** per serving

ready in 20 minutes,
plus cooling and setting

11.5g sachet of sugar-free
raspberry jelly crystals

2 tsp powdered gelatine

225g strawberries

300g raspberries

150g blueberries

fresh mint sprigs, to decorate

fat free natural fromage frais,
sweetened to taste, to serve

Fresh strawberries, raspberries and blueberries are suspended in a tasty raspberry jelly: if ever a dessert had the wow factor, it's this one!

Put a 900g loaf tin in the freezer to chill.

Following the packet instructions, dissolve the jelly crystals in water to make 600ml of jelly liquid.

Put 2 tablespoons of hot (but not boiling) water in a small bowl and sprinkle over the gelatine powder. Stir well until it is completely dissolved, then stir the mixture into the jelly liquid. Leave the mixture to cool.

Put all the fruit in the chilled loaf tin and pour in the jelly mixture. Cover the tin with a piece of baking parchment, a large plate and a few cans or weights to stop the fruit bobbing up. Chill for 4 hours or until the jelly is firmly set.

When you're ready to eat, fill a large bowl with hot water and dip the sides of the loaf tin in the water for 5 seconds. Hold a serving plate over the top of the tin and flip it over quickly to turn out (shake the tin gently if it needs a little help).

Cut into slices and divide between plates. Decorate with mint sprigs and serve with fat free natural fromage frais.

individual rhubarb crumbles

Our clever mini crumbles use biscuits and oats to give sensational stewed rhubarb a tempting low-Syn topping.

Preheat the oven to 200°C/Fan 180°C/Gas 6.

Put the rhubarb on a baking tray and sprinkle with 4 tablespoons of water and the sweetener. Bake for 10 minutes then remove from the oven.

Meanwhile, make the crumble topping. Put the biscuits in a sealable food bag with the oats, ginger and 1 teaspoon of cinnamon and roughly crush with a rolling pin.

Sprinkle the remaining cinnamon over the rhubarb, stir well and divide between four ramekins or small pie dishes. Sprinkle the crumble on top and bake for 20 minutes or until nicely browned.

Serve hot with dollops of fat free natural fromage frais.

If you can't imagine crumble without custard, go for low fat custard from a can or carton – 3 tablespoons adds 2 Syns.

serves 4

4½ Syns per serving

ready in 40 minutes

10 rhubarb sticks, trimmed and cut into 7cm pieces

6 tbsp sweetener

3 reduced fat digestive biscuits

1 level tbsp plain porridge oats

¼ tsp ground ginger

2 tsp ground cinnamon

fat free natural fromage frais, sweetened to taste, to serve

mississippi mud pie

serves 10

5½ Syns per serving

ready in 30 minutes, plus cooling and setting

60g low fat spread

10 reduced fat digestive biscuits

10 sheets of leaf gelatine

200ml skimmed milk

4 level tbsp cocoa powder, plus 1 tsp to dust

2 tsp coffee granules

250g quark

3 x 175g pots Muller Light Vanilla yogurt (or any Free vanilla yogurt)

4 tbsp sweetener

5g milk chocolate, grated, to decorate

Everyone will enjoy our show-stopping lighter version of the much-loved American chocolate dessert.

Preheat the oven to 190°C/Fan 170°C/Gas 5 and line an 18cm springform tin with non-stick baking parchment.

Melt the spread in a pan over a low heat.

Meanwhile, put the biscuits in a sealable food bag, bash into fine crumbs and tip into a bowl. Pour in the melted spread, stir well and spoon the mixture into the prepared tin to cover the base, pressing down evenly. Bake for 12-15 minutes then set aside to cool.

Meanwhile, put the gelatine sheets into a small bowl, cover with cold water and leave to soften for 5 minutes.

Mix the milk, cocoa powder and coffee granules in a jug and heat in the microwave for 2 minutes. Squeeze the excess liquid from the gelatine sheets, add the sheets to the milk and whisk until they have dissolved. Leave to cool for 10 minutes.

Whisk the quark, yogurt, sweetener and cooled milk using a hand whisk and pour on to the biscuit base. Chill for 4 hours or until set.

Release the pie from the tin and put the pie, still on its base if necessary, on a serving plate. Sprinkle over the grated chocolate and extra cocoa and slice to serve.

lemon ice cream

serves 4

4½ Syns per serving

ready in 30 minutes,
plus freezing

___

2 tbsp sweetener

400g low fat custard
from a can or carton

2 x 175g pots Muller Light
Vanilla yogurt (or any
Free vanilla yogurt)

finely grated zest of
2 large unwaxed lemons,
plus extra to decorate

2 egg whites*

*Pregnant women, the
elderly and babies are
advised not to eat raw
or partially cooked eggs.

On a hot summer's day nothing refreshes like an ice cream – and our lip-licking lemon variety will help everyone beat the heat.

Put the sweetener, custard, yogurts and lemon zest in a food processor.

Beat the egg whites lightly until frothy, then add to the food processor and blend to combine. Check the flavour, adding more sweetener if you like.

Pour the mixture into an ice cream maker (or see tip, below) and churn for 15-20 minutes or until softly set. Pour the mixture into a shallow freezer-proof container and freeze for 2 hours or until firm enough to scoop.

Pop the ice cream into the fridge for 10-20 minutes before serving so that it can soften a little.

Scatter over the extra lemon zest to decorate.

If you don't have an ice cream maker you can still make this delicious ice cream. To stop ice crystals forming, just beat the mixture – by hand or in a food processor – three times during the freezing process.

peach melba

serves 4

1½ Syns per serving

ready in 30 minutes

200g fat free natural
Greek yogurt

2 tsp sweetener

600g raspberries,
plus extra to decorate

8 peaches, peeled,
stoned and sliced

1 ginger nut biscuit, crushed

This legendary peach and raspberry dessert was created at London's Savoy Hotel and named after Dame Nellie Melba, the Australian opera star. Melba toasts are named after her too!

Mix the yogurt and half of the sweetener in a bowl.

Put half of the raspberries and the remaining sweetener in a food processor or blender and whizz to a smooth purée.

Line the bases of four dessert glasses with most of the peach slices then add layers using up most of the whole raspberries and all of the raspberry purée. Spoon the yogurt on top.

Decorate each glass with the remaining peach slices and raspberries, and scatter over the biscuit crumbs to serve.

apple betty

Apples take a starring role in our take on the traditional fruit dessert, infused with the delicious sweetness of cinnamon.

Preheat the oven to 190°C/Fan 170°C/Gas 5.

Arrange the apple slices in a 20cm flan dish and sprinkle over most of the sultanas.

Beat the eggs with the sweetener and vanilla extract, then add the yogurt and beat again.

Pour the eggs over the apples and sultanas and let them sink in to the fruit. Scatter over the remaining sultanas, dust with cinnamon and bake for 30 minutes or until set.

Serve warm with fromage frais.

serves 6

2½ Syns per serving

ready in 40 minutes

---

2 large eating apples, peeled, cored and sliced

50g sultanas (or use raisins)

8 eggs

4 tbsp sweetener

2 tsp vanilla extract

175g pot Muller Light Vanilla yogurt (or any Free vanilla yogurt)

pinch of cinnamon, to dust

fat free natural fromage frais, sweetened to taste, to serve

black forest choc pots

serves 4

5 Syns per serving

 (without the fromage frais)

ⓥ

ready in 20 minutes,
plus cooling and freezing

35g dark chocolate
(70% cocoa), broken
into small pieces

2 large eggs, separated*

2 tbsp sweetener

300g fat free natural
fromage frais

1 tsp vanilla extract

425g can pitted black cherries
in light syrup, drained

*Pregnant women, the
elderly and babies are
advised not to eat raw
or partially cooked eggs.

Succulent cherries and indulgent chocolate
mousse combine to create a sweet sensation
in these fabulous pots inspired by the classic
German gâteau.

Melt 30g chocolate in a large, heatproof bowl set over a pan of gently
simmering water. Remove from the heat and leave to cool slightly at
room temperature.

Meanwhile, put the egg whites in a large, clean glass bowl and beat
with an electric hand whisk set to medium until stiff peaks form.

Put the egg yolks and 1 tablespoon of sweetener in another bowl.
Whisk until smooth then stir this into the melted chocolate.

Using a metal spoon, carefully fold the egg whites into the chocolate
until well combined. Spoon into four freezer-proof glasses or ramekins
and freeze for 1 hour or until just set.

Just before you want to eat, beat the fromage frais, vanilla extract and
remaining sweetener until well combined. Spoon the mixture over each
dessert, top with the cherries and grate over the remaining chocolate
to serve.

banana
fritters

Banana fans will love these desert island discs!
We've served them with extra banana and a big
dollop of fromage frais.

Put three bananas in a large bowl and mash with a fork. Add the eggs,
flour, cinnamon and sweetener and beat well.

Spray a large non-stick frying pan with low calorie cooking spray and
place over a medium-high heat. Working in batches, drop heaped
tablespoons of the mixture into a pan. Cook for 2 minutes or until
the undersides are firm and golden then flip and cook for another
2 minutes or until cooked through. Transfer to a plate, cover and keep
warm until you have used all the mixture – you should have enough to
make about 16.

Slice the remaining bananas and divide between plates along with the
fritters. Add a dollop of fromage frais and dust with cinnamon to serve.

*For an extra-sweet treat, spoon over a little honey
just before you serve (1 Syn per level teaspoon).
For extra zing, sprinkle over a little grated
lime zest.*

serves 4

4 Syns per serving

ready in 20 minutes

5 medium bananas

2 eggs, lightly beaten

25g self-raising flour

1 tsp cinnamon, plus
extra to dust

1 tsp sweetener

low calorie cooking spray

fat free natural fromage frais,
sweetened to taste, to serve

cook's tips

eggs

Pregnant women, the elderly and babies shouldn't eat raw or partially cooked eggs. We'll make a note in any recipes where raw or partially cooked eggs are used.

fat free natural fromage frais, quark and yogurt

These are wonderful ingredients when you're Food Optimising as they give the creamy texture and taste normally achieved with cream. However, they tend to separate when boiled and can make the dish look unappetising. So unless the recipe says otherwise, add yogurt, quark or fromage frais off the heat once all the other ingredients have been cooked and simply heat through. They make great savoury or sweet ingredients – if you're using them to top a pudding, add sweetener and maybe some vanilla essence as well, to taste.

fresh, canned and frozen

Frozen ingredients and canned veg and beans are great alternatives to fresh foods and are so handy to keep in the cupboard or freezer. They'll keep for much longer, can be quicker to cook and are just as good for you. So feel free to switch between all three – bear in mind cooking times may change slightly.

fresh herbs

These lose their freshness quickly so if you have more than you can use, freeze them in a little water in ice cube trays – then you can add them straight to stews and curries.

fruit

While most fresh whole fruit is Free, puréed or cooked fruit counts as Syns because it isn't as filling and becomes much easier to over-consume. You'll see that in any recipes where fruit is puréed or cooked, we've counted it as Syns.

low calorie cooking spray

To cut down on fat in recipes, we recommend using non-stick cookware/bakeware wherever possible. However, where you do need to use fat then choose a low calorie cooking spray which contains 1 calorie or less per spray, as these are Free – others would need to be counted as Syns. Ideal for fried eggs, roast potatoes and chips!

meat and poultry

Trim off any visible fat before cooking to make lean meat or poultry Free, and remember to remove the skin before or after cooking poultry. If you cook poultry with the skin on, cook it separately from the other ingredients so that the fat can't run into them (eg don't roast potatoes in the same tin).

measurements

Syns for some ingredients are based on level teaspoons or tablespoons. Without measuring carefully, it's easy to far exceed your intended Syn intake without realising – so scrape a knife along the top of the spoon, knocking the excess back into the container. For best results, invest in a set of measuring spoons.

minced meat and poultry

Lean minced meat (5% fat or less) is a Free Food. Beef, pork and turkey mince are available in most major supermarkets at 5% fat or less – check the nutrition information to be sure. If possible, drain off any fat that comes from the mince while you're cooking it. No chicken and lamb mince is widely available with 5% fat or less so these would have a Syn value… unless you know a friendly butcher who'll mince skinless chicken breasts or lean lamb with all visible fat removed for you.

mustard powder

Made-up mustard in jars has Syns because it contains Synned ingredients while mustard powder is Free, making it a great choice for dressings and sauces.

seasoning

Where salt and pepper are used, we usually suggest seasoning to taste. Official advice is that adults should eat no more than 6g of salt a day – and bear in mind that small amounts can quickly add up.

stock

Fresh stock, stock cubes, stock pots, bouillon powder, ready-to-use liquid stock and liquid stock concentrate are all Free but be aware that gravy granules or powder and stock granules are not. Stock should normally be boiling when you add it to the pan, as cold stock will slow down cooking times.

symbol sense

ready in…

This gives a guide to how long the recipe will take to prepare and cook.

serves…

This gives you an idea of how many people the recipe can serve. However, feel free to split the recipe between more or fewer people instead, depending on how hungry you are – especially when it's Free!

freezer-friendly ❄

Recipes showing this symbol can be safely frozen for up to 1 month. Keep in mind official advice on freezing safely:

- Label food for the freezer with details of what the meal is and when you cooked it.

- Make sure food has cooled before you put it in the freezer.

- Defrost frozen meals completely and reheat thoroughly before eating.

Batch cooking: Wherever you see the freezer-friendly symbol ❄, you can save time and effort by cooking double or triple amounts and freezing the rest to enjoy at a later date. You'll usually save money too because it's often cheaper to buy ingredients in bulk.

suitable for vegetarians Ⓥ

Recipes marked with this symbol are suitable for vegetarians. Recipes that contain meat, fish or poultry can often be made vegetarian by using Quorn mince or pieces, textured vegetable protein/soya protein or tofu instead. Some ingredients that are unsuitable for vegetarians might surprise you so always check the packaging to be sure.

Extra Easy *SP*

For super-charged weight loss, go for dishes marked Extra Easy *SP*. Ask your Slimming World Consultant for more details.

index